SOUR, RAW, COLD...

# PHILOSOPHY OF HEALTH

Anna Ciesielska

Publisher: CENTRUM ANNA UK Ltd
Suite U505A Threshold and Union House
65-69 Shepherds Bush Green
London W12 8TX

Centrum Anna UK Ltd website address is:
www.centrumanna.co.uk

First Published by Centrum Anna, 1998

English edition published by Centrum Anna UK Ltd, 2014
English version © Agnieszka H. Pabianek, 2014

Anna Ciesielska asserts the moral right to be identified as the author of this work

A catalogue record for this book
is available from the British Library

Paperback ISBN      978-0-9926519-0-9
.epub ISBN          978-0-9926519-1-6
.mobi ISBN          978-0-9926519-2-3

Printed in Great Britain

Although every effort has been made to ensure the contents of this book are accurate, it must not be treated as a substitute for qualified medical advice. Always consult a medical practitioner. Neither the author nor the publisher can be held responsible for any loss or claim arising out of the use, or misuse, of the information and suggestions contained in this book, or the failure to take medical advice.

# CONTENTS

INTRODUCTION TO THE ENGLISH VERSION      9

INTRODUCTION      13

THE UNIVERSAL TRUTH OF TAO      19

THE PRINCIPLES OF CHINESE MEDICINE      29

YIN-YANG, THE FIVE ELEMENTS THEORY AND THE HUMAN BODY      32

INTERNAL BODILY ORGANS ACCORDING TO THE PRINCIPLES OF
CHINESE MEDICINE      38

     Circulation/sex ................................................................. 39
     Triple heater .................................................................. 39
     Liver and gall bladder ........................................................ 42
     Heart and the small intestine ................................................ 47
     Spleen (pancreas) and stomach .............................................. 49
     Lungs and the large intestine ................................................ 53
     Kidneys and urinary bladder ................................................. 55
     Energetic peaks and lows of bodily organs and their meridians .................. 58

FACTORS AFFECTING THE BALANCE OF YIN-YANG WITHIN THE BODY      60

     Flavours ....................................................................... 60
     Climates ....................................................................... 69
     Emotions ...................................................................... 75
     Colours ........................................................................ 81
     Movement – physical activity ................................................. 86

DEFICIENCIES AND EXCESSES OF ENERGY WITHIN THE BODY      88

TONGUE      96

DISEASES      98

     Obesity ....................................................................... 102
     Problems with cholesterol .................................................... 107

Osteoporosis . . . . . . . . . . . . . . . . . . . . . . . . . . . . . . . . . . . . . . . . . . . . . . . . . . . . . . . . . . 108

Allergies . . . . . . . . . . . . . . . . . . . . . . . . . . . . . . . . . . . . . . . . . . . . . . . . . . . . . . . . . . . . . . . 110

Peptic ulcer disease and gastric hyperacidity . . . . . . . . . . . . . . . . . . . . . . . . . . . . . . . 112

Diabetes . . . . . . . . . . . . . . . . . . . . . . . . . . . . . . . . . . . . . . . . . . . . . . . . . . . . . . . . . . . . . . . 114

Coeliac disease . . . . . . . . . . . . . . . . . . . . . . . . . . . . . . . . . . . . . . . . . . . . . . . . . . . . . . . . . 115

Cystic fibrosis . . . . . . . . . . . . . . . . . . . . . . . . . . . . . . . . . . . . . . . . . . . . . . . . . . . . . . . . . . 116

Our problems with children . . . . . . . . . . . . . . . . . . . . . . . . . . . . . . . . . . . . . . . . . . . . . . 117

Old age and its ailments . . . . . . . . . . . . . . . . . . . . . . . . . . . . . . . . . . . . . . . . . . . . . . . . . 119

Examples of the effectiveness of the therapies proposed in this book . . . . . . . . . . . . 123

## NUTRITION AND HEALTH                                                            127

Vitamins and mineral salts . . . . . . . . . . . . . . . . . . . . . . . . . . . . . . . . . . . . . . . . . . . . . . . 129

## FOOD PRODUCTS                                                                   138

Dairy . . . . . . . . . . . . . . . . . . . . . . . . . . . . . . . . . . . . . . . . . . . . . . . . . . . . . . . . . . . . . . . . . . 138

Meat . . . . . . . . . . . . . . . . . . . . . . . . . . . . . . . . . . . . . . . . . . . . . . . . . . . . . . . . . . . . . . . . . . . 143

Vegetables . . . . . . . . . . . . . . . . . . . . . . . . . . . . . . . . . . . . . . . . . . . . . . . . . . . . . . . . . . . . . 153

Legumes . . . . . . . . . . . . . . . . . . . . . . . . . . . . . . . . . . . . . . . . . . . . . . . . . . . . . . . . . . . . . . . 156

Nuts . . . . . . . . . . . . . . . . . . . . . . . . . . . . . . . . . . . . . . . . . . . . . . . . . . . . . . . . . . . . . . . . . . . 157

Fruit . . . . . . . . . . . . . . . . . . . . . . . . . . . . . . . . . . . . . . . . . . . . . . . . . . . . . . . . . . . . . . . . . . . 158

Cereal . . . . . . . . . . . . . . . . . . . . . . . . . . . . . . . . . . . . . . . . . . . . . . . . . . . . . . . . . . . . . . . . . 160

Bread . . . . . . . . . . . . . . . . . . . . . . . . . . . . . . . . . . . . . . . . . . . . . . . . . . . . . . . . . . . . . . . . . . 160

Pasta . . . . . . . . . . . . . . . . . . . . . . . . . . . . . . . . . . . . . . . . . . . . . . . . . . . . . . . . . . . . . . . . . . 161

Grains . . . . . . . . . . . . . . . . . . . . . . . . . . . . . . . . . . . . . . . . . . . . . . . . . . . . . . . . . . . . . . . . . 162

Cakes and biscuits . . . . . . . . . . . . . . . . . . . . . . . . . . . . . . . . . . . . . . . . . . . . . . . . . . . . . . 164

Sugar and sweets . . . . . . . . . . . . . . . . . . . . . . . . . . . . . . . . . . . . . . . . . . . . . . . . . . . . . . . 165

Drinks . . . . . . . . . . . . . . . . . . . . . . . . . . . . . . . . . . . . . . . . . . . . . . . . . . . . . . . . . . . . . . . . . 167

Fats . . . . . . . . . . . . . . . . . . . . . . . . . . . . . . . . . . . . . . . . . . . . . . . . . . . . . . . . . . . . . . . . . . . . 180

Herbs and spices . . . . . . . . . . . . . . . . . . . . . . . . . . . . . . . . . . . . . . . . . . . . . . . . . . . . . . . . 183

## BALANCED NUTRITION                                                              185

## RECIPES                                                                         191
## SOUPS

Breakfast Soup . . . . . . . . . . . . . . . . . . . . . . . . . . . . . . . . . . . . . . . . . . . . . . . . . . . . . . . . . 191

Chicken and Beef Broth . . . . . . . . . . . . . . . . . . . . . . . . . . . . . . . . . . . . . . . . . . . . . . . . . . 192

Tomato Soup . . . . . . . . . . . . . . . . . . . . . . . . . . . . . . . . . . . . . . . . . . . . . . . . . . . . . . . . . . . 193

Egg Noodles . . . . . . . . . . . . . . . . . . . . . . . . . . . . . . . . . . . . . . . . . . . . . . . . . . . . . . . . . . . . 193

Ukrainian Borscht . . . . . . . . . . . . . . . . . . . . . . . . . . . . . . . . . . . . . . . . . . . . . . . . . . . . . . . 194

Bean Soup .................................................. 195
Pearl Barley Soup ............................................ 196
Onion Soup ................................................. 197
Split Pea Soup .............................................. 197
Soup à la Napolitana ........................................ 198
Sweet Cabbage Soup ......................................... 198
Small Round Noodles Soup .................................... 199
Beetroot Leaf Soup .......................................... 200
Button Mushroom Soup ....................................... 201
Green Pea or Corn Soup ...................................... 202
Leek Soup .................................................. 202
Gold Vegetable Soup ......................................... 203
Celeriac Soup ............................................... 204
Spring Soup................................................. 204
Vegetable Soup .............................................. 205
Sorrel Soup ................................................ 206
Sour Rye Soup .............................................. 207
Autumn Soup ............................................... 208
Clear Borscht ............................................... 208
Summer Split Pea Soup ....................................... 210

VEGETARIAN RECIPES

Boiled Potatoes ............................................. 211
Pancakes ................................................... 211
Sweet Cabbage Stuffing ...................................... 212
Sweet White Cheese Stuffing .................................. 212
Fried Bananas ............................................... 212
White Cheese Gnocchi ....................................... 213
Omelette with Button Mushrooms ............................. 213
Potato Pancakes ............................................. 214
Pearl Barley Croquettes ...................................... 214

MEAT AND MEAT-VEG RECIPES

Risotto .................................................... 215
Meat and Vegetable Stuffing (for pancakes) .................... 216
Meat Marinade .............................................. 216
Pork Breaded Cutlets ........................................ 216
Ribs with Cabbage ........................................... 217
Spicy Ribs .................................................. 218

Stewed Sweet Ribs . . . . . . . . . . . . . . . . . . . . . . . . . . . . . . . . . . . . . . . . . . 218
Roast Loin of Pork . . . . . . . . . . . . . . . . . . . . . . . . . . . . . . . . . . . . . . . . . . 219
Roast Pork . . . . . . . . . . . . . . . . . . . . . . . . . . . . . . . . . . . . . . . . . . . . . . . . . . 220
Meat Balls . . . . . . . . . . . . . . . . . . . . . . . . . . . . . . . . . . . . . . . . . . . . . . . . . . 221
Mince burger . . . . . . . . . . . . . . . . . . . . . . . . . . . . . . . . . . . . . . . . . . . . . . . . 222
Stewed Pork with Vegetables . . . . . . . . . . . . . . . . . . . . . . . . . . . . . . . . . . 222
Loin of Pork with Bacon and Button Mushrooms . . . . . . . . . . . . . . . . . . 223
Roast Beef . . . . . . . . . . . . . . . . . . . . . . . . . . . . . . . . . . . . . . . . . . . . . . . . . . 224
Beef with Cabbage . . . . . . . . . . . . . . . . . . . . . . . . . . . . . . . . . . . . . . . . . . . 224
Beef Roll . . . . . . . . . . . . . . . . . . . . . . . . . . . . . . . . . . . . . . . . . . . . . . . . . . . 225
Beef Stew with Vegetables . . . . . . . . . . . . . . . . . . . . . . . . . . . . . . . . . . . . 226
Béchamel Sauce (for cooked chicken meat used previously in a broth) . . . . . . . . . . 227
Green Béchamel Sauce . . . . . . . . . . . . . . . . . . . . . . . . . . . . . . . . . . . . . . . . 227
Chicken Breast (with sage and vodka) . . . . . . . . . . . . . . . . . . . . . . . . . . . . 228
Chicken Breast with Pineapple . . . . . . . . . . . . . . . . . . . . . . . . . . . . . . . . . 228
Chicken in Breadcrumbs . . . . . . . . . . . . . . . . . . . . . . . . . . . . . . . . . . . . . . 229
Traditional Roast Chicken . . . . . . . . . . . . . . . . . . . . . . . . . . . . . . . . . . . . . 229
Roast Chicken with Onion . . . . . . . . . . . . . . . . . . . . . . . . . . . . . . . . . . . . . 230
Roast Duck with Stuffing . . . . . . . . . . . . . . . . . . . . . . . . . . . . . . . . . . . . . . 230
Roast Chicken with Stuffing . . . . . . . . . . . . . . . . . . . . . . . . . . . . . . . . . . . 231
Roast Turkey with Stuffing . . . . . . . . . . . . . . . . . . . . . . . . . . . . . . . . . . . . 231
Fried Fish (fillets) . . . . . . . . . . . . . . . . . . . . . . . . . . . . . . . . . . . . . . . . . . . 231
Fish in Vegetables . . . . . . . . . . . . . . . . . . . . . . . . . . . . . . . . . . . . . . . . . . . 232

## SIDE VEGETABLES

Stewed Carrots . . . . . . . . . . . . . . . . . . . . . . . . . . . . . . . . . . . . . . . . . . . . . . 233
Stewed Vegetables (carrots, pea and kohlrabi) . . . . . . . . . . . . . . . . . . . . . 233
Beetroot Salad . . . . . . . . . . . . . . . . . . . . . . . . . . . . . . . . . . . . . . . . . . . . . . . 234
Beetroot with Horseradish . . . . . . . . . . . . . . . . . . . . . . . . . . . . . . . . . . . . . 234
Warm Beetroots . . . . . . . . . . . . . . . . . . . . . . . . . . . . . . . . . . . . . . . . . . . . . 235
Stewed Sauerkraut with Button Mushrooms . . . . . . . . . . . . . . . . . . . . . . . 235
Cabbage and Carrot Salad . . . . . . . . . . . . . . . . . . . . . . . . . . . . . . . . . . . . . 236
Cauliflower Salad . . . . . . . . . . . . . . . . . . . . . . . . . . . . . . . . . . . . . . . . . . . . 236
Stewed Cabbage with Tomatoes . . . . . . . . . . . . . . . . . . . . . . . . . . . . . . . . 237
Stewed Pattypan Squash/Courgette . . . . . . . . . . . . . . . . . . . . . . . . . . . . . . 237
Stewed Sweet Pepper . . . . . . . . . . . . . . . . . . . . . . . . . . . . . . . . . . . . . . . . . 238
Red Cabbage Salad . . . . . . . . . . . . . . . . . . . . . . . . . . . . . . . . . . . . . . . . . . . 238
Stewed Red Cabbage . . . . . . . . . . . . . . . . . . . . . . . . . . . . . . . . . . . . . . . . . 238
Stewed Vegetables . . . . . . . . . . . . . . . . . . . . . . . . . . . . . . . . . . . . . . . . . . . 239

Fried Vegetables . . . . . . . . . . . . . . . . . . . . . . . . . . . . . . . . . . . . . . . . . . . . . . . . . . . . . . . . . . . 240
Canned Green Bean Salad . . . . . . . . . . . . . . . . . . . . . . . . . . . . . . . . . . . . . . . . . . . . . . . . . . 240
Canned Green Peas Salad . . . . . . . . . . . . . . . . . . . . . . . . . . . . . . . . . . . . . . . . . . . . . . . . . . 240

SALADS FOR SUPPER
Vegetable Salad with Marinated Pepper and Sweet Corn . . . . . . . . . . . . . . . . . . . . . . 241
Vegetable Salad with Tomatoes . . . . . . . . . . . . . . . . . . . . . . . . . . . . . . . . . . . . . . . . . . . . 241
Chicory, Pepper and Radish Salad . . . . . . . . . . . . . . . . . . . . . . . . . . . . . . . . . . . . . . . . . 242
Reddish Salad . . . . . . . . . . . . . . . . . . . . . . . . . . . . . . . . . . . . . . . . . . . . . . . . . . . . . . . . . . . . 242
Cress and Lettuce Salad . . . . . . . . . . . . . . . . . . . . . . . . . . . . . . . . . . . . . . . . . . . . . . . . . . 243
Tomato and Lettuce Salad . . . . . . . . . . . . . . . . . . . . . . . . . . . . . . . . . . . . . . . . . . . . . . . . 243
Pea Salad I . . . . . . . . . . . . . . . . . . . . . . . . . . . . . . . . . . . . . . . . . . . . . . . . . . . . . . . . . . . . . . 244
Pea Salad II . . . . . . . . . . . . . . . . . . . . . . . . . . . . . . . . . . . . . . . . . . . . . . . . . . . . . . . . . . . . . 244
Egg Salad (Paste) . . . . . . . . . . . . . . . . . . . . . . . . . . . . . . . . . . . . . . . . . . . . . . . . . . . . . . . . 245
Traditional Vegetable Salad . . . . . . . . . . . . . . . . . . . . . . . . . . . . . . . . . . . . . . . . . . . . . . 245
Tuna or Sardine Salad . . . . . . . . . . . . . . . . . . . . . . . . . . . . . . . . . . . . . . . . . . . . . . . . . . . 246
Smoked Mackerel Salad (Paste) . . . . . . . . . . . . . . . . . . . . . . . . . . . . . . . . . . . . . . . . . . 246

SUPPER DISHES
Hungarian Style Sausage . . . . . . . . . . . . . . . . . . . . . . . . . . . . . . . . . . . . . . . . . . . . . . . . . 247
Sweet Corn Sauce (for pastas) . . . . . . . . . . . . . . . . . . . . . . . . . . . . . . . . . . . . . . . . . . . . 248
Pizza . . . . . . . . . . . . . . . . . . . . . . . . . . . . . . . . . . . . . . . . . . . . . . . . . . . . . . . . . . . . . . . . . . . . 248
Tartare Sauce . . . . . . . . . . . . . . . . . . . . . . . . . . . . . . . . . . . . . . . . . . . . . . . . . . . . . . . . . . . . 249
Ham Hock in Jelly . . . . . . . . . . . . . . . . . . . . . . . . . . . . . . . . . . . . . . . . . . . . . . . . . . . . . . . 250
Homemade Pâté . . . . . . . . . . . . . . . . . . . . . . . . . . . . . . . . . . . . . . . . . . . . . . . . . . . . . . . . 251
Lard with Spices . . . . . . . . . . . . . . . . . . . . . . . . . . . . . . . . . . . . . . . . . . . . . . . . . . . . . . . . 252

CAKES
Chocolate Sponge Cake . . . . . . . . . . . . . . . . . . . . . . . . . . . . . . . . . . . . . . . . . . . . . . . . . . 252
Yellow Sponge Cake . . . . . . . . . . . . . . . . . . . . . . . . . . . . . . . . . . . . . . . . . . . . . . . . . . . . . 253
Coconut Cake . . . . . . . . . . . . . . . . . . . . . . . . . . . . . . . . . . . . . . . . . . . . . . . . . . . . . . . . . . . 254
Birthday Cake . . . . . . . . . . . . . . . . . . . . . . . . . . . . . . . . . . . . . . . . . . . . . . . . . . . . . . . . . . . 255
Ginger Bread à la Granny Sophie . . . . . . . . . . . . . . . . . . . . . . . . . . . . . . . . . . . . . . . . . 256
Apple Cake . . . . . . . . . . . . . . . . . . . . . . . . . . . . . . . . . . . . . . . . . . . . . . . . . . . . . . . . . . . . . 256
Strawberry Cake . . . . . . . . . . . . . . . . . . . . . . . . . . . . . . . . . . . . . . . . . . . . . . . . . . . . . . . . 257
Spicy Honey Balls . . . . . . . . . . . . . . . . . . . . . . . . . . . . . . . . . . . . . . . . . . . . . . . . . . . . . . . 258

TEA, COFFEE, COCOA
Neutral Tea I (good for everyone) . . . . . . . . . . . . . . . . . . . . . . . . . . . . . . . . . . . . . . . . . 258

Neutral Tea II (good for everyone) ............................................. 259
Date Tea ............................................................................. 259
Boiled Coffee ...................................................................... 259
Boiled Cocoa ...................................................................... 260

PRESERVES
Plum Jam ............................................................................ 260
Plum and Banana Jam .......................................................... 261
Apricot Jam ........................................................................ 261
Pear Compote ..................................................................... 261
Whole Tomatoes .................................................................. 262

RECIPES FOR WARMING AND STRENGTHENING DISHES
Beef Broth .......................................................................... 262
Lamb Broth ........................................................................ 263
Energizing Beef Broth ........................................................... 263
Energizing Lamb Broth .......................................................... 264
Stewed Lamb ...................................................................... 264
Beef Stewed in Red Wine ....................................................... 264
Stewed Carrot ..................................................................... 265
Carrot Soup ........................................................................ 265
Fried Garlic ........................................................................ 265
The 'Killer' Warming Tea ....................................................... 266
Ginger Tea ......................................................................... 266
Boiled Coffee with Ginger (Cinnamon or Cardamom) ................... 266
Red Indian's "Drink of Life" ................................................... 266
Grog ................................................................................. 267
Goat's Milk ........................................................................ 267

SUGGESTIONS FOR BREAKFASTS, DINNERS AND SUPPERS          267

SUMMARY                                                                          271

LIST OF FOOD PRODUCTS ACCORDING TO THE FIVE ELEMENTS THEORY          284

FOOD PRODUCTS OF COOLING PROPERTIES                          285

SOUR, RAW AND COLD FOOD PRODUCTS                              286

# INTRODUCTION TO THE ENGLISH VERSION

Remain calm and trust the wisdom and knowledge revealed to you in this book. It is based on and is coherent with the Order of this world and applies to all the areas and peoples of the Earth. Once you begin to understand its rules, this knowledge will shield and protect you. Our grandmothers and great-grandmothers used their intuition on many occasions to appropriately treat certain food products and secure the wellbeing of their families. Nowadays, there are still a few places on Earth where people live accordingly to traditional rules and maintain a well-balanced diet.

After years of fascination with vitamins and antibiotics, it is time to go back to Nature (the Order) and respect its laws and rules. They have an impact on everyone, at all times and in every corner of the Earth – whether one is conscious of it or not. Therefore my reflections on illnesses and their causes are also universal and apply to everyone.

What is the message I send to you in this book? Simple – to cook! I recommend a well-balanced diet based on a variety of products available to us, a diet that is rich in flavours and easy to digest and absorb. The recipes I include in this book are well balanced, both in flavour and energetically. They are based on traditional Eastern European cuisine, but are also universal. You can use them as a starting point for creating your own recipes, respecting at the same time your own traditions and habits, as well as the Order of the world. By implementing such a diet you will regenerate your body, rid it of chronic ailments and illnesses, and, in the case of more serious health problems, it will give you support, pain relief or even healing.

You must remember that a good diet is the first step to protecting your health and life. The quality of the food you eat has an impact on how you feel, how you behave, what emotions are dominant in you, what decisions in life you make. Therefore you should always treat cooking, and food in general, with appropriate respect; the time spent on preparing food is never wasted.

I am confident that if you follow what I share with you in my books, you will become more conscious of the surrounding reality – the energy of colours, flavours and different food products. You will realize that your life is a unity and depends on the decisions you make every day.

Anna Ciesielska

*'I am grateful that destiny has allowed me to turn the fruits of my work and life into this book.'*

# INTRODUCTION

I would like to dedicate this book to all of those who strive for a peaceful, healthy and harmonious life, and who, at the same time, experience anxiety on and off caused by their powerlessness against the enormity of suffering and disease.

In this book you will not find any of those popular, but unverified, Western dietary novelties. The content of this book is based entirely on my personal knowledge and years of experience, which I gained through a thorough study and examination of the ancient philosophy of the East. I looked particularly carefully into Chinese medicine, which is established in relation to the universal laws of Nature and the Cosmos and which can bring order in life and all its aspects. Throughout the centuries, many societies and civilizations have learnt to respect and live by these rules. Hippocrates, commonly referred to as the 'Father of Medicine', believed that one should do no harm but seek help in the healing powers of Nature. The Hippocratic Oath, which has become the foundation for good medical practice and morals, contains a very important statement. It says that every doctor, as a matter of obligation to their profession, should always pursue and expand their knowledge so that it may be of benefit to the sick. In his medical studies, Hippocrates dedicated much attention to the importance of a healthy diet and the nature of the food we eat. He is the author of a famous saying: *'Let food be thy medicine and medicine be thy food'* and *'food can bring you health, but it can also kill'*.

However, the main aim of this book is not to rewrite the philosophy of the East or to create new terms or definitions. I would rather leave that to those who have the drive and passion to argue about Tao in an intriguing, profound and humorous way. Instead, I would rather use their 'ready-made' statements, terms and definitions in order to draw for you in a very simple manner the core sense and universalism of this philosophy.

In this book I am also not trying to get to the bottom of diagnosis or treatment according to Chinese medicine. I only signal the way this kind of medicine treats the human body and what it uses in order to help people. My main aim here is to explain that its core principle is to prevent disease.

In accordance with the Taoist philosophy, I try to explain the major functions of bodily organs, the relationships between them and the influence of a particular diet on their functioning. This is a book on how to translate the universal knowledge and wisdom of the surrounding world into the language of good nutrition. Let us trust the Creator. Let us begin to utilize the benefit of what has been given to us here on Earth to enrich us, to make us happier and healthier.

We must wake up and start appreciating the surrounding world because absolutely everything we need to keep us healthy is out there. There is no laboratory that could give us reasonable solutions to our suffering and illnesses. These solutions we must find within ourselves, in our openness, sincerity, trust and simplicity. It is not the bacteria and viruses that destroy us but our own ignorance and mistrust towards the things we have been given by Nature to live in good health.

We usually seek solutions to our problems in elaborate and complicated scientific research programmes and processes. And as it turns out, the solutions are much simpler. We need only to learn how to direct our efforts in the opposite direction, towards ourselves, towards our households, and to infuse them with reason, intuition and responsibility.

If we could realize the meaning of the Order both here on Earth and in the Cosmos, we would be able to experience authentic freedom, the kind of freedom that allows us to live normally and humanly, to self-create, to make a conscious decision about the quality of our life. This may all sound incredible but it is the truth. We can start creating a world of order and harmony and begin benefiting from its plentiful goodness.

People do not have to be ill, miserable and tired all the time, although we cannot deny that suffering is one of the unavoidable elements of human life. In fact, suffering is important for our transformation and development. However, suffering should not dominate our life. If it does, then it becomes a mere burden and loses its positive side. We should be able to be free from unnecessary suffering. One must remember that suffering can lead to aggression, impatience, malice, doubt and insecurity. And these are the elements that dominate modern societies. It is tragic that people, and children and youth in particular, do not realize their suffering, do not understand that life can be different. Such feelings as compassion, openness, empathy, love, peace and tolerance can only be characteristic of healthy and happy people. And these are exactly the feelings that we should aspire to and cherish.

I wish people would start believing that they have the power to decide their own health and wellbeing. This book is meant to show the way to total freedom in the entirety of the meaning of this word. The knowledge that is revealed in this book will free everyone from their insecurities, fears and suffering. By following the book on an everyday basis, life will be perceived as more valuable and we will become calmer and more stable.

Throughout my whole adult and ailing life I was troubled by many questions. Why am I ill even though I am trying to live in accordance with the common knowledge? Why do those who look after themselves fall ill the same as those who do not? Why do all of those dietary and nutrition guidelines seem to be so ineffective? And throughout the years I remained driven by the thought that there must be some universal principles of proper nutrition. I was certain that we are making a crucial mistake in our attempts to stay healthy by following all kinds of vitamin treatments. At the peak of my troublesome journey, I discovered the principles of Chinese medicine. These classic rules about bodily organs, the physiology of the body according to the Yin-Yang concept, and the Five Elements Theory, as well as the whole Taoist philosophy, were like a true revelation to me, which soon became a signpost to an understanding of the forces of life and its meaning. It was at this point that I decided to look more closely into these theories and investigate whether and how they can be applied in relation to our climatic realities, eating habits and traditions and how they can affect our life. For many years I have studied the nature of our everyday food products and their influence on our health. I tried to find out if there was a logical connection between those products and the most common health issues. The more I began to understand for myself, the more horrified I was. I realized that it is really down to us if we want to sustain the good quality of our life and how little is needed in order to have healthy babies, to stop small children from being ill, to keep our youth calm and even-tempered, to stop our life being a misery and prevent constant visits to the health centre and the pharmacy, to make our old age independent, happy and peaceful. Thanks to this newly gained consciousness, I started noticing the number of mistakes that people make, mistakes which derive directly from their lack of knowledge and which lead to illnesses and the suffering of their loved ones.

For many years I struggled to find the right way of communicating my knowledge to people. On one hand, I could see the fantastic effects of application of this knowledge in everyday life; on the other hand, I realized that it is quite complex. It started growing on me and eventually I was sure that I needed to share this knowledge with people and help them in their suffering. I chose a form that would be easy to understand for everyone. I became convinced that I could simplify my message to the necessary minimum so that it could be easily applied in everyday life. I left the details and nuances to doctors, researchers, specialists and enthusiasts. I only wish for myself that everyone would live their life according to this knowledge. What you will find here is a recipe for life. My advice and suggestions have been verified and are safe. This is a primer to the rules of Nature and everyone should learn it the same way a child learns reading and writing. A more thorough analysis on the impact of food on our body, however, can be found in my next publication.

I do realize that this book is not perfect. But I do hope that it will become an inspiration for further reflection on life and the eventual transformation of our lifestyle. Perhaps in the future I will be able to create, together with the help of my readers, a database on food and its impact on our health, in which we will all share our knowledge and experiences. Maybe in this way we will be able to secure a normal childhood for our children that will be free of illnesses, suffering or fear. This is my most profound dream.

Healthy diet requires respect for knowledge, wisdom and experience. Otherwise we end up with the ridiculous modern diets which are in direct opposition to thousands of years of experience. Their mistakes are difficult to realize at first. After many years they will reveal themselves as certain health dispositions and diseases. I would rather advise you to lean towards the wisdom and experience of hundreds of generations.

I would also like to emphasize that you should treat this book as a whole. Anyone trying to only pick and choose a few bits and pieces here and there may end up coming to the wrong conclusions and eventually doing harm to themselves. The best way to comprehend it all is to read the book a few times.

# THE UNIVERSAL TRUTH OF TAO

Great masters believe Tao to be inexplicable and inconceivable.

> *Tao is beyond words and beyond things.*
>
> *It is not expressed either in word or in silence.*
>
> *Where there is no longer word or silence Tao is apprehended.*
> (The Way of Chuang Tzu)

Within the Universe there exists a certain Order, which leads to harmony and balance. Co-existence of Nature and humans is the major element of harmony on Earth. Tao can be perceived via observation of the processes of Nature.

Nature is a teacher to us all. When people start messing with the laws of Nature they enter the path of self-destruction. Men and Nature create one whole, they become Tao. Human life is an inseparable element of the general natural process that in its substance becomes the essence of the Universe. The art of life should resemble more a navigational process than a military campaign. It is important to understand the winds, tides, changes, the seasons of the year, principles of growth and death. One must learn how to use them and not fight with them.

> *I tried to find what Order is. I was excited about it, and I wrote many, many words of what Order is. Every time I wrote something, I felt it wasn't quite enough. If I had covered, say, two thousand pages with just words of what Order is, I would not be satisfied with this statement. And then I stopped by not saying what it is, just saying, "Order is."*

*And somehow I wasn't sure it was complete until I asked*
*somebody, and the person I asked said, "You must stop right*
*there. It's marvellous; just stop there, saying: Order is."*
(Louis I. Kahn)

Tao is referred to as the Way, Reason, Providence, Absolute and God, but God not in the sense of a ruler, monarch or lord and master. Tao is the eternal Order, Nature's Way, the Source of life and change within the Universe.

*The Way brings form,*

*Its Virtue Fosters them,*

*With matter they take shape,*

*And circumstance perfects them all:*

*That is why all things*

*Do honour to the Way*

*And venerate its power.* (Lao Tzu 'The Way')

*There is no other way but The Way.* (Lao Tzu)

Tao is most often compared to Water. Water is the essence of life and the earthly equivalent of Tao. The so-called Stream Way, in Tao terms, represents the way of life with all its vitality and struggle. This is because Water is the most powerful of all elements.

*Water is yielding, but all-conquering. Water extinguishes*
*Fire or, finding itself likely to be defeated, escapes as*
*steam and reforms. Water washes away Soft Earth, or*
*when confronted by rocks, seeks a way round. Water*
*corrodes Iron till it crumbles to dust; it saturates the*
*atmosphere so that Wind dies. Water gives way to obstacles*

*with deceptive humility. For no power can prevent it following its destined course to the sea. Water conquers by yielding; it never attacks, but always wins the last battle.*
(The successor of the Old Master)

Tao constitutes the most durable reality and energy within the Universe; it is the foundation of both the existent and non-existent.

*Tao is the watercourse way of the Universe – it constitutes its only organizing principle.*
(Alan Watts)

It can be found in the unformed order of calm waters, in the shapes of trees and clouds, in the structure of crystals of frost or in the pattern of stones lying on a beach.

Fig. 1. The Yin-Yang symbol with white representing Yang and black representing Yin.

*The Supreme Artisan made the Universe like a great zither upon which he placed as it were strings to yield a variety of sounds. A harmonious chord is sounded by spirit and body, angel and devil, heaven and hell, fire and water, air and earth, sweet and bitter, soft and hard, and so are all other things harmonized.* (Honorius of Autun – 1125)

21

All things within the Universe are of a bipolar nature. Yin and Yang are two poles of Cosmic energy. The relationship between them is a symbolic manifestation of the processes within Tao. In a more conventional way, Yin is symbolized by minus (-) and Yang by plus (+). Yin and Yang are inseparable, interdependent and defining each other. Yang cannot exist without Yin and Yin without Yang. In every Yin there is an element of Yang and vice versa. Together they create a passionate and inseparable pair, the same as a woman and a man or Sky and the Earth.

The Yin-Yang principle also translates as a necessary relationship between 'something' (Yin) and 'nothing' (Yang), activity and non-activity, a solid and space, dream and awakening, return to existence and nonexistence. Material examples of this can be an empty vessel (nothing inside of something) or a window (we can see something through nothing). It can also relate to cold and warmth, weakness and strength, condensation and dispersion, evil and good, calmness and activity, sadness and happiness, death and birth. It is also the energy of the Earth (Yin) and Sky (Yang).

Tao is also a 'rhythmical motion' or 'going forward', where 'going' means Yang and 'stopping' means Yin (Wieger).

The principle of Yin-Yang becomes the source for processes and phenomena within the Universe and on Earth. It is a constant wrestle and struggle of two opposite elements. However, it is not a struggle leading to domination.

In life, one should not pursue Yang with a simultaneous avoidance of Yin but sustain equilibrium between these two elements, because one cannot exist without the other. A human being is not perfect and certain flaws are even needed to strengthen one's character. One should be able to accept good and evil, which are inseparable. However, it is necessary to keep control over the struggle between these elements. Otherwise it can lead to destruction and an imbalance in both the social and personal life of an individual. Yin and Yang are two different aspects of the same unity, like two sides of a coin. If one of them disappears, the whole system is at risk.

The human body possesses internal intelligence (the reason of the body) similar to that of Nature's ecosystem. Thus, the intelligence of our bodies, our impulses and senses, should be under continuous scrutiny. They provide us with information on our needs. The important thing is the ability to interpret this information.

The human body is a precise example of a Yin-Yang system. The human brain is comprised of two hemispheres, the left and right. The right hemisphere (Yin) is responsible for the left side of the body, representing irrationalism, intuition, femininity and sensitivity. The left hemisphere (Yang) is responsible for the right side of the body, and stands for rationalism, masculinity and firmness. Thus, the world should be perceived from this dual perspective: as irrational and rational, sensitive and firm, feminine and masculine. But one must remember to maintain a balance between the two sides of this equation. Only then will our own perception of reality be just and allow us to be open to new experiences.

Unfortunately, development in the sciences has led to exposure of the left hemisphere and simultaneous degradation of the right one. Intuition and the subconscious have been reduced to a minimal role. Our thinking has been influenced by a set of rational symbols and laws to the point that only through them are we able to define reality. We have relegated responsibility for our own health to doctors and scientists and we no longer ask questions about the mystery of creation, growth and death. Through a multigenerational denial of the right hemisphere, the intuition and unconscious within us have gone into hibernation.

At the beginning of the 20th century, together with the development of quantum physics, many physicists began to realize the numerous problems facing humanity. They suggested that spiritual enlightenment is extremely important for the reorganization of the traditional way of thinking and seeing reality as one big whole. According to them, interdependence, symmetry and polarization are basic rules constituting the physical world. The physical Universe is an entirety made of two opposites (left and right) which should stay in balance. Mass and energy or time and space are merely two opposite aspects of the same matter. These scientists realized that the classical philosophy of the East (the Yin-Yang theory) provides the same understanding of life processes as quantum theory. They think that the philosophy of the East and the philosophy of modern physics both lead us to spiritual enlightenment. They claim that we are the key to the understanding of the Universe and that only we can influence the surrounding reality.

The way Nature is constructed is in fact an obstacle on the road to its cognition and analysis. Thus, scientific truth does not have much in common with the real truth of Nature. However, the previously mentioned physicists, they do realize that the world of science would oppose and deny the philosophy of spiritual enlightenment. The rational perception of the world and reality is strongly rooted in people's consciousness and it would be difficult for them to open up to the possibility of spiritual creation.

In the 9th century BC, Chuang Tzu described this problem as follows. He said that a frog in a well is not able to imagine an ocean, and a summer bug will never comprehend ice. How then can a scientist comprehend Tao when they are limited by their own scientific boundaries?

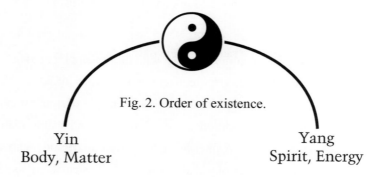

Fig. 2. Order of existence.

Yin
Body, Matter

Yang
Spirit, Energy

Spirituality in human life is yet another manifestation of Yin-Yang; it is a state of equilibrium between matter and energy, Body and Spirit. The Body (Yin) manifests the existence of energy (Yang). The Body invites energy into our existence and energy moves the Body and gives it life. In other words, Yin, with its durability, supports Yang and Yang stimulates Yin. Wanting to increase our spirituality, we have to strive for the development and improved quality of both aspects simultaneously. It is impossible to develop and increase the quality of Yang (Spirit) without a simultaneous development and increase in the quality of Yin (Body).

In order to illustrate, in a more thorough way, the nature of our surrounding reality, Taoist philosophy uses natural cycles and processes and refers to them as the Five Elements Theory (Fig. 3). Both theories, the Yin-Yang theory and the Five Elements Theory, describe the mutual influence of man and Tao. Five Elements create a system of interdependences between processes, agents, phases, movements, stages, transformations or powers, where one of the elements cannot exist without all of the others. You cannot exclude one element without the destruction of the whole system. This is the foundation for treating the Universe as an organic and interrelated entirety. The Cosmos manifests itself in every single thing. Thus, anything can be treated as being the heart of the Universe.

In the Five Elements Theory, the basic elements are represented by: Wood, Fire, Earth, Metal and Water. The trajectory of creation can be explained as follows: Wood generates Fire; Fire creates ashes, which turn into Earth; Earth yields Metal; Metal gives beginning to Water; Water generates Wood by nourishing its growth. This constitutes the nutrient cycle of the elements (see Fig. 5).

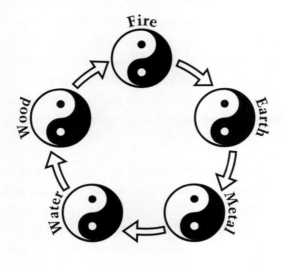

Fig. 3. Five Elements Theory.

The elements maintain their internal harmony through a system of mutual checks, known as control cycles (see Fig. 6). Wood protects the vitality of Earth and creates conditions conducive to its optimal quality. Earth controls Water and restrains its violence. Water extinguishes Fire and stops it from spreading. Fire melts Metal and makes it flexible. Metal cuts Wood and protects us from its expansive powers.

The Five Elements Theory (see Tab. 3) determines the natural habitat of man. It stands for seasonal change, climates, tastes and colours. Within the human body, it represents the solid and empty bodily organs, senses, structural elements, emotions and cycles of growth.

The Five Elements Theory and Yin-Yang theory, in Chinese medicine, form the basis for the prevention, diagnosis and treatment of illnesses. They are the foundation of dietetics, herbal medicine and acupuncture (acupressure). The application of Yin-Yang without the Five Elements Theory leads to an incomplete treatment of the human body.

Yin-Yang and the Five Elements Theory bring order within Tao. However, they are not its laws.

# THE PRINCIPLES OF CHINESE MEDICINE

In Chinese medicine, Man and the Universe are treated as one whole. Everything depends on harmony and a free flow of energy. And that is the basic principle of this 'medicine of unity'.

Man originates from the Cosmos and becomes a micro-cosmos himself (the word 'cosmos' derives from Greek, meaning 'order'). The energy that enlivens the human body comes straight from the Universe. Good health is a state of balance between all kinds of ubiquitous energies: material, spiritual and psychological. The medicine of the West avoids treating the human body as a whole and strives for a narrowed-down specialization. Chinese medicine, instead of removing man from Nature (the Cosmos) and analysing particular bodily organs, treats the human body as an entirety that belongs to the Universe.

Chinese medicine is commonly known because of the popularity of acupuncture. But one should not disregard the fact that it is most of all the 'medicine of unity'. It treats the human body as a physical, emotional and spiritual entirety. Thus, a disease is no more than an interruption in the flow of energy caused by its excess or deficiency. Energy should be allowed to circulate within a body without any obstructions. It should flow between all the organs of the body and should also connect the body with the mind and soul. If the flow of energy is interrupted or restricted at any point it manifests itself in the form of disease. This is the basic principle of Taoist emptiness. Nothing should block the energy (of life). Its circulation must be free. The free movement and flow of energy keeps the balance within the human body.

Nutrition, herbs and acupuncture are the three major tools used in Chinese medicine to fight an imbalance of energy.

Apart from dealing with diseases, Chinese medicine teaches us a certain perception of the world. The human body is in fact nothing but a reflection of our own relationship with the Universe. This type of medicine allows us to feel part of Nature, not only in a social or human context. It actually shows us that we can exist and live in harmony with everything that surrounds us.

The feelings that we experience in life, such as aggravation or calmness, happiness or sadness, love or hatred, are part of a cycle that conducts our existence. If one of these elements should be missing, the whole balance and harmony is disturbed. This applies also to colours, tastes and smells, which should connect to their symbolic equivalents derived from Nature. Any imbalance within these elements leads to imbalance within ourselves.

In Taoist philosophy, a human is symbolized ideographically as a Tree rooted in the Earth with its branches directed towards the Sky (Fig. 4).

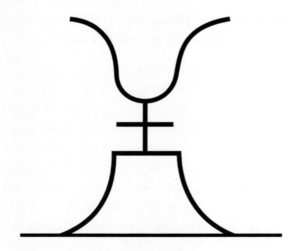

Fig. 4. Ideogram of a human according to Tao.

The lower part of the ideogram, opened towards Earth, symbolizes the physiology of the whole human body, beginning from simple cells and culminating in highly specialized structures. Chinese medicine deals with this whole area.

The upper part of the ideogram, directed towards the Sky, represents human spirituality, which participates in all the substantial processes within the Universe. This area relies on impulses and energies that escape cognition. It is the area of our existence which cannot be explained by common terminology, symbolism or scientific logic. Within this area, even the most open-minded specialists can face difficulties when trying to solve extreme cases of diagnosis and treatment.

In the centre of the ideogram, between the Sky and the Earth, is a cross that separates the physiological and spiritual levels. It also secures the exchange between the Spirit and the Body and becomes a bridge between humans and the Universe. In this way, a human derives strength equally from beneath and from above, is supported by Earth and transformed by Sky.

According to Chinese medicine the best remedy for disease is prevention.

> *Maintaining order rather than correcting disorder is the ultimate principle of wisdom. To cure disease after it has appeared is like digging a well when one feels thirsty or forging weapons after the war has already begun.* (Chinese quotation)

# YIN-YANG, THE FIVE ELEMENTS THEORY AND THE HUMAN BODY

According to the Yin-Yang theory, there are internal bodily organs Yin and Yang. The internal bodily organs Yin (solid bodily organs) are the liver, heart, spleen, lungs and kidneys. The pancreas, in Chinese medicine, is treated as part of the spleen. Solid bodily organs absorb, transform and store energy essential to life.

The internal bodily organs Yang (empty bodily organs) consist of the gall bladder, the small intestine, stomach, the large intestine and urinary bladder. They are responsible for the digestion, excretion and supply of energy to the internal bodily organs Yin.

| Yin | Yang |
|---|---|
| dark | bright |
| cold | hot |
| wet | dry |
| closed | open |
| concave | convex |
| gentle | steep |
| focused | expansive |
| descending | ascending |
| passive | active |
| calm | violent |
| slow | fast |
| feminine | masculine |
| night | day |
| heavy | light |
| internal | external |

Table 1. Universal model of YinYang.

| Yin | Yang |
|---|---|
| Production of blood, lymph, hormones, nutritious substances, collagen, urine, sweat, tears, mucus, sputum, pus and fat. | Circulation, respiration, heartbeat, metabolism, peristalsis, excretion. |

Table 2. Physiological model of Yin-Yang.

Every solid bodily organ represents moisture (Yin) received through the blood. However, in order to function well they also require energy (Yang). On the other hand, Yang bodily organs represent dryness, and in order to function well they need moisture, mucus and all sorts of nutritious internal fluids. And so, the gall bladder needs bile, the small intestine and stomach need digestive juices and mucus, the large intestine needs mucus and nutritious fluids, and the urinary bladder needs urine.

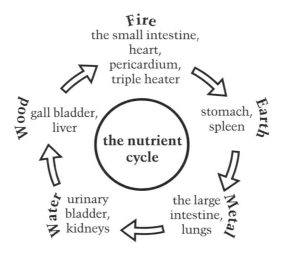

Fig. 5. The nutrient cycle.

The spleen is thought to be the Yin root of the body. It produces all the internal fluids, such as blood and nutritious fluids. The Yang root of the body is the right kidney. It gathers and stores the afterbirth warmth as well as the warmth received from food. It then directs it to the rest of the bodily organs. Both roots depend on the strength and efficiency of the stomach, which stands at the gate of our physical existence. And it is the stomach that supplies the spleen with the energy that is obtained from food as well as the provisionally processed essence.

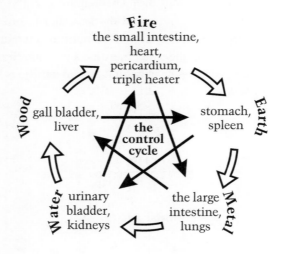

Fig. 6. The control cycle.

Yin-Yang defines the opposites and the Five Elements Theory describes the functioning of bodily organs and dependencies between them. The Five Elements represent five groups of bodily organs. Each element is ascribed one solid bodily organ (Yin) and one empty bodily organ (Yang).

- Wood = liver and gall bladder

- Fire = heart and the small intestine

- Earth = spleen (pancreas) and stomach

- Metal = lungs and the large intestine

- Water = kidneys and urinary bladder

The interdependencies between these bodily organs are similar to those between particular elements. They can be observed within the nutrient and control cycles (see Fig. 5 and Fig. 6). The bodily organs interact with each other through stimulating and strengthening or restricting and controlling their functions. The most powerful bodily organs are those ascribed to the element of Earth. They are the stomach, spleen and pancreas.

| Equivalents | Wood | Fire | Earth | Metal | Water |
|---|---|---|---|---|---|
| Solid bodily organs (Yin) | Liver | Heart, pericardium | Spleen | Lungs | Kidneys |
| Empty bodily organs (Yang) | Gall bladder | The small intestine, triple heater | Stomach | The large intestine | Urinary bladder |
| Senses | Eyes, sight | Tongue, speech | Mouth, taste | Nose, smell | Ear, hearing |
| Other bodily organs, tissues | Nails, tendons, short muscles | Arteries, blood | Subcutaneous tissue, long muscles | Skin, bodily hair | Bone marrow, brain, teeth, hair, genitals |
| Secretions | Tears | Sweat | Saliva | Mucus | Urine |
| Life cycle | Birth | Education | Work | Retirement | Dying |

| Growth cycle | Birth | Growth | Maturity | Old age | Death |
|---|---|---|---|---|---|
| Influence | Calming | Inspirational, cognitive, wisdom | Harmonizing, concentrating | Openness, space | Courage, internal will power |
| Emotions | Anger, irritation, hatred | Joy, infantile laughter | Care, concern, compassion | Sadness, sorrow | Fear, depression |
| Proneness to | Swearing, screaming | Laughing | Singing | Crying | Groaning |
| Influence of bio-climate | Wind | Heat | Humidity | Dryness | Cold |
| Sides of the world | East | South | Centre | West | North |
| Seasons | Spring | Summer | Late summer | Autumn | Winter |
| Times of day | Morning | Noon | Afternoon | Evening | Night |
| Tastes | Sour | Bitter | Sweet | Hot | Salty |
| Smells | Sour and rancid smelling | Smell of burning | Nice and sweet smell | Irritating, strong and pervading smell | Rotten smelling |
| Types of meat | Chicken, duck | Lamb, goat meat | Beef, veal, goose, rabbit | Horse meat, wild boar, venison, turkey | Pork, fish, pigeon |

| Types of grain | Wheat | Rye, buck-wheat | Corn, millet | Oat, rice | Bean, soya |
|---|---|---|---|---|---|
| Food pres-ervation | Fer-menting, pickling | Smoking | Candying | Coating in hot spices, vacuum packing | Salting, freezing |
| Ways of cooking | Short steaming without a lid | Grill, spin-ning grill | Stewing in a small amount of water without stirring | Pressure cooker | Cooking in a large amount of water with stirring |
| Colours | Green | Red | Yellow, gold | White, silver | Black |
| Stones | Turquoise | Coral | Amber | Mountain crystal | Black onyx |

Table 3. Equivalents of the Five Elements.

# INTERNAL BODILY ORGANS ACCORDING TO THE PRINCIPLES OF CHINESE MEDICINE

In order to better understand the functions and properties of bodily organs in accordance with the Five Elements Theory and Yin-Yang, see the picture below. These rules will enable comprehension of the mechanism of excesses and deficiencies in bodily organs which lead to imbalance within the body and consequently to particular symptoms and ailments. These rules also explain how to eliminate the causes of such imbalance. It is not complicated and I will illustrate it through this simple example.

| TAO | | | |
|---|---|---|---|
| **YIN** | | **YANG** | |
| Substance, body | Blood, internal fluids | Energy | Warmth |

Fig. 7. Four roots of a single bodily organ.

Our body (Yin) is like an oil heater inside which circulates the oil (blood and internal fluids). In order to make this heater work properly we need energy Yang (Chi) to stimulate the oil and produce warmth. If Chi goes missing, the warmth is still there. However, if there is a shortage of oil the heater will not work, even if Chi and warmth are present. Chi and warmth may be there, but if there is no oil the heater will simply burn out. This also happens with our body. Destructive agents, such as inappropriate food (flavours), colours and climates will destroy Yang (that is Chi and warmth), whereas Yang associated with emotions will destroy internal fluids.

**A deficiency of Yin is normally caused by a deficiency of Yang. If we want to strengthen our body we must strengthen Yin and Yang simultaneously.**

**If our body is weakened we must not warm it up (Yang) before we balance out our internal substances and fluids (Yin). We do not need much time to strengthen the Yang of our bodily organs (warmth and Chi), whereas reconstruction of our substances and fluids requires a longer period of time.**

Apart from the five basic groups of internal bodily organs, each one of which is ascribed to one of the Five Elements, there also exist two other bodily functions that belong to the element of Fire. These are: **circulation/sex** and **triple heater**.

## Circulation/sex

Circulation/sex regulates the flow of arterial and venous blood as well as the internal and external secretion of the gonads. It is responsible for blood pressure and clarity of mind. It is also called 'the ministry of joy'. Circulation/ sex represents the energy of the Sky (Yang). It is directly connected to the functioning and energy of the liver. A strong liver, on the other hand, enables the proper flow of energy, fluids and a good quality of mind. Circulation/sex is often weakened by an ineffectual and cold spleen.

## Triple heater

The human body consists of three parts; each one of them is ascribed an important function.

- Located from the navel downwards is the bottom heater. It contains two primary energies which are linked with the energies of the middle and the upper heater.

- Located from the naval up to the solar plexus is the middle heater. Here, energy is received from food.

- The upper heater is located between the solar plexus and the neck and arms. Here energy is received from air.

The triple heater starts to function from the moment we are born. For the proper development of the body, all three parts must function well.

The middle heater comprises those bodily organs which are responsible for the digestion of food and the transfer of essence and energy. These are the stomach, spleen, pancreas and liver. The most important organ of them all is the stomach. Dependent on its activity and efficiency is the appropriate quantity and quality of energy that is then transferred to the spleen.

The spleen transforms this energy into essence and internal bodily fluids and passes them on to the lungs. The functioning of the stomach and the spleen is supported by the liver and pancreas. If the stomach and spleen are malfunctioning and do not receive energy from food, then the middle heater cannot fulfil its role. **The cause of 90% of all illnesses is in fact a cold stomach and spleen, or in other words, an inactive middle heater.** In order to function well the middle heater must be supplied with the right quality of food. The food should be adjusted to the specific needs and requirements of a single organism and be rich in energy. Energy cannot be obtained from nothing. And we very often forget or do not realize how important an agent energy is when it comes to our health. The stomach will only function well when it is warm. Only then is it able to transfer energy to the spleen and support the functions of life.

The upper heater is comprised of the lungs and heart. The spleen transfers the essence and Chi (energy) to the lungs. At this point, the energy of food joins the energy of air. By breathing properly and deeply, and breathing in fresh air, we generate an appropriate quantity and quality of energy. A proper body posture, as well as physical exercise, can also 'fill' us with energy. A well-functioning upper heater translates to a well-functioning heart and circulatory system. On the other hand, a malfunctioning middle heater leads to a shortage of energy to the upper heater, which manifests itself as lung and heart diseases. And it is the lungs that are responsible for the transfer of essence and energy to the lower heater.

The lower heater is comprised of the kidneys and genitals. The lower heater maintains our life energy; it is like a fire boiling a kettle, inside of which energy is being transformed into matter and vice versa – matter into energy. Thanks to this process, our metabolism functions properly. The most important organs within the lower heater are the kidneys, and especially the right kidney, called the kidney of Fire. It emanates the warmth of our life energy Yang. A new-born baby is given two types of energy: the energy of its parents and the energy of the macro-cosmos. Both of these constitute our personal energy of life and our duty is to preserve it. We can achieve this through proper breathing, and a good diet and lifestyle. If we fail to do so, our life energy runs out fast. The core of the Taoist system is to keep and store this energy and to continuously strengthen it by producing and adding even more energy.

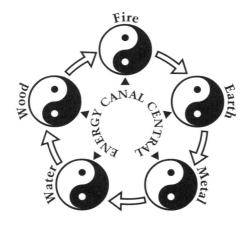

Fig. 8. Flow of energy from within
the central canal.

All three energies meet at a point located slightly below the kidneys. From there, as a unity, they travel to the central canal located alongside the spine (see Fig. 8).

From the central canal the energy goes first to the bodily organs Yang (empty bodily organs). They then transform this energy into energies suitable for particular bodily organs Yin (solid bodily organs). From the bodily organs Yin, the energy starts travelling within the whole body. Some of this energy is stored by the bodily organs Yin (energy banks), in case of an illness, and some of it is passed on to the kidneys as super-essence.

The above description of the triple heater highlights the true meaning and importance of warmth and energy within our body. By taking care of all three heaters we can secure our life energy and ensure good health.

## Liver and gall bladder

The energetic peak for the liver (element of Wood) occurs between 1a.m. and 3a.m., and for the gall bladder between 11p.m. and 1a.m. (see Fig. 10).

The liver controls the tendons, ligaments, muscles, eyes, nails, peripheral nerves and genitals. It is also responsible for the production of bile and tears. The meridian of the liver is intertwined around the internal reproductive organs and therefore affects their proper functioning and overall condition. Within the nutrient cycle, the liver represents the element of Fire, providing a sufficient supply of cleansed blood to the heart. The heart rate is dependent on the strength and condition of the liver. The condition of the liver, on the other hand, depends on the functioning of the element of Earth (spleen) and the corresponding quantity of Water (as supplied by the kidney). The functioning of the liver is comparable to the awakening of spring (the season associated with increased energy, motion and life), which at the same time is controlled and limited by the contrasting element of Metal (lungs).

According to the Five Elements Theory, the liver (Wood) is a crucial link in the cycle of energy. However, as for the other elements – Metal, Fire and Water, it relies on the Centre, referred to as Mother Earth. The liver also controls the element of Earth and sets the direction of energy flow in both of the meridians of the spleen and stomach. The liver's energy enriches the quality of the element of Earth, prevents it from general heaviness, passiveness and hardness. The benefits of the liver's influence on the spleen are not merely physical or physiological but also emotional.

The liver represents the subconscious, the heart the mind and the spleen the conscious. The subconscious registers everything without having to analyse and calculate particular experiences. Thus, analogically, a well-functioning liver directly influences the condition of both the mind and the conscious. Any kind of imbalance in the functioning of the liver can be responsible for a malfunctioning of the mind. This usually demonstrates itself in the form of aggression, anger, tension, nervousness, etc. A well-functioning liver also ensures a good quality of sleep. If the liver fails or malfunctions, the quality of sleep can be badly affected.

The functioning of the liver always depends on the quantity and quality of blood. The production of blood is a responsibility of the spleen; it generates fluids and, with the help of the kidneys and bone marrow, transforms them into blood.

There are many commonly known conditions (and their symptoms) that can affect the liver. When applying certain treatments we usually eliminate pain, forgetting, at the same time, about the source of the pain. Every condition affecting the liver highlights an imbalance of Yin-Yang or the stalling of energy together with the stalling of blood.

A wrong diet, bad emotional states and coldness can lead to all of the above problems.

The major cause of a cold liver is a lack of Yang. To the typical symptoms of a cold liver belong: weak ligaments and tendons, curved spine, eye problems, but also problems with nails and reproductive organs, as well as hernias and a swelling of the testicles. The ultimate consequence of a chronically cold liver is cirrhosis. To its initial symptoms belong flatulence and indigestion.

Hepatitis, on the other hand, is a consequence of a cold liver and a cold spleen, with the latter producing large quantities of mucus. In the case of malaria, together with a cold liver and a cold spleen, the humidity of the climate is another influential factor accelerating the course of the disease.

A cold liver is caused by a deficiency of Yang (warmth) and Chi within the whole body. It is a very severe and dangerous condition. The root of this disease starts with a cold spleen and kidneys. And as it happens, the stomach, spleen and kidneys are the organs that are first affected by any destructive situation.

When dealing with a cold liver, one should eliminate food of the Yin nature and switch to homemade food. All daily meals should be warm and cooked with additional appropriate herbs and spices.

A deficiency of blood in the liver (deficiency of Yin) is a result of a dysfunction of the spleen. This is the initial cause of liver fire. However, if the blood deficiency is treated in time, the liver fire can be eliminated and the balance re-established.

To the most common symptoms of a deficiency of blood in the liver belong: painful and light-sensitive eyes, white and broken nails, muscular contractions (at night in particular), shaking hands and legs, rather weak menstrual bleeding (or a complete lack of it), dizziness, hair loss, weakened sight and blurred vision.

To the symptoms of liver fire belong: dryness of the eyes, broken and splitting nails, redness of the face, red eyes, emotional aggravation, difficulties with falling asleep and insomnia, headaches, dizziness, nose bleeds, a yellow discharge for women, prostatitis, haematuria (blood in the urine), arthritis, psoriasis, excessive sweating at night, hyperthyroidism, ligament and muscular contractions.

All bodily organs are affected by a deficiency of Yin in the body (that is, a deficiency of blood and bodily fluids). However, there are specific symptoms indicative of the malfunctioning of particular bodily organs. A deficiency of Yin in the liver affects the heart, lungs and also the kidneys. But very often the impact of the imbalance of Yin in the liver on other bodily organs is overlooked. Rarely do we realize that the true cause of, for example, arthritis, is in fact a liver dysfunction and/or spleen dysfunction. We also do not realize that modification of our eating habits could significantly benefit our health. Faced with liver and spleen dysfunctions, one should immediately eliminate all food of the Yin nature. Any treatment by antibiotics would not help in this case, for we are not dealing here with an infection.

The imbalance of Yin in the liver (the so-called liver fire) is very difficult to treat and restore to its original state. Often, the devastation within the body has gone too far and the damage of the bodily organs is too severe. However, by implementing a new form of diet, one can stop the progress of a disease. A well-balanced diet can, in fact, ease or even eliminate all the ailments.

In the situation of a blood deficiency and liver fire, one should focus on extinguishing the fire and, on the other hand, strengthening the spleen and the left kidney in order to restore the right level of Yin. Therefore, despite all the heat within the body, one must not extinguish it with water (literally) or cold food. This might only augment problems with the spleen, cause a deficiency of Yin and, consequently, lead to liver fire.

The level of Yin and the intensity of fire in a bodily organ can be assessed by a careful observation of symptoms occurring just before and during the energetic peak of this particular organ. Excess of Yang will manifest itself during the energetic peak, whilst deficiency of Yang will show during the energetic low. For example, when in the late evening or at night, we crave something sour or sweet, it means that there is a deficiency of Yin in the liver (deficiency of blood). This does not necessarily signify the fire, but it is indeed a symptom of a certain imbalance within the body and one should immediately concentrate on strengthening one's spleen.

Apart from deficiency of Yin or Yang, the liver can also be badly affected by the stalling of energy Chi and blood. This usually happens during an emotional shock, frustration or stress, or may be caused by overeating or a low body temperature.

A stalling of Chi in the liver makes it lose control over the flow of energy in the meridians of the stomach and spleen. It leads to specific problems, such as stomach aches and contractions, flatulence, nausea, vomiting, headaches, a feeling of pressure inside the chest, weakness, shivering or loss of appetite. Long-lasting stalling in the liver can ultimately cause a cold liver. If there is a stalling of Chi and blood in the liver, one must absolutely avoid sour food; this would only exacerbate the liver dysfunction. What one needs in such a case is spicy and warm food that would propel the flow of energy and blood.

One of the bodily organs located next to the liver is the gall bladder. It provides the liver with energy from the central canal. It also stores bile produced by the liver, and bile is absolutely necessary for the emulsification of fat from food. The condition of both organs is dependent on their mutual interaction. It is best for the liver if the gall bladder is at ease and functioning properly. To achieve this state, one must eat warm food of a neutral warming nature. Any excess of sour food will cause contraction of both organs and will eventually lead to difficulties with the digestion of fat.

The energetic canal of the gall bladder begins in the outer corners of the eyes, then it runs all around the head, through the neck and arms, chest, and the outer side of the hips into the feet. Therefore it has a great impact on all sorts of muscular contractions (mainly those of the neck, hips, legs and feet), headaches, on the quality of breathing and on the energy flow within the so-called 'miraculous canal' that encompasses the whole body. This particular canal controls the flow of energy between the lower and upper parts of the body. Within the canal there is a special spot, which is located on the foot and is responsible for muscular flexibility and proper flow of energy.

One of the symptoms of a deficiency of blood in the liver is stiffness of the body and mind. Deficiency of blood in the liver always leads to a blockage of the gall bladder and, eventually, gallstones. Gallstones, a very common condition of the gall bladder, are caused firstly by a cold liver, then by a stalling of blood and Chi in the liver, and lastly by the stalling of bile in the gall bladder. This particular condition of the gall bladder has a direct impact on the liver, which manifests itself by occurrence of liver stones and liver fire.

## Heart and the small intestine

The energetic peak for the heart occurs between 11a.m. and 1p.m., and for the small intestine between 1p.m. and 3p.m. (see Fig.10).

The heart sets blood into circulation and its function depends on the energy Chi and blood. Heart failures occur when the lungs stop delivering an adequate quantity of Chi into the blood. The heart merges blood with the Spirit (our intelligence). However, in order for this to happen our mind needs to be clear (state of a clear heart).

The heart controls the arteries, our outer appearance (skin, complexion), the tongue and mouth, inner corners of the eyes, blood and sweat.

The ability for verbal expression belongs to the element of Fire. The heart represents love, compassion, responsibility and also our mind. Thus, all mental illnesses are a consequence of heart problems.

Within the nutrient cycle, and according to the Five Elements Theory, Fire is generated by Wood (Fire = heart, Wood = liver). Therefore, in order for the heart to function properly, the liver should contain an adequate quantity of Chi and blood. The Fire, through its warmth, energy and good blood circulation, supports and enriches the Earth (spleen, stomach). Fire is also responsible for the warming up of the kidneys (Water).

The heart controls Metal and overcomes its tendency to brooding and sorrow. The heart makes Metal more flexible and adaptable. Water, on the other hand, controls and prevents Fire from destroying the fragility of the essence and Yin, and from drying out the body.

A weak and cold spleen is the main cause of heart disease. Whenever the spleen suffers from a deficiency of Yang, it will try to obtain it instead from the element of Fire (heart); this weakens the heart and blood circulation. Therefore, those who have suffered a heart attack have a significantly enlarged spleen. A malfunctioning liver can also badly affect the heart, as can the following: a cold liver, a stalling of energy and blood, deficiency of blood in the liver and liver fire.

Also, lung diseases, deficiency of Chi, deficiency of both Yin and Yang, or an excess of mucus or cold kidneys can all lead to heart failures and problems with blood circulation.

To the most common symptoms of a weakened heart (deficiency of Yang) belong: tachycardia, sweating during the day, difficulties in breathing, a white or blue face, general weakness, sensitivity to cold, weak breath, pressure within the chest, heart pain, depression and fear.

All of the above symptoms can be a warning signal to an impending heart attack.

To the symptoms of a blood deficiency (heart fire) belong: profuse sweating at night, poor sleep, speech disorders, palpitations, mouth ulcers, redness of the face, dark urine, haematuria, constipation and aggravation.

On the other hand, blue lips and a sharp pain within the chest signify a stalling of Chi and blood.

As the heart is totally dependent on the other organs of the body, in order to maintain the wellbeing of the heart, one should consciously take care of the following:

- a proper diet (spleen, stomach)
- a good quality of breathing (lungs)
- good emotional states (liver, spleen)

- cold prevention (kidneys)

- plenty of relaxation and sleep (liver, spleen).

One should especially follow all the above recommendations when dealing with mental illnesses. The most important of them all is a proper diet; good food can bring balance to the element of Earth and consequently to our consciousness. And a balanced consciousness, in other words, means a calm and peaceful mind.

The heart is also interlinked with the small intestine. The small intestine transforms the energy from the central canal and then delivers it to the heart. The small intestine can also protect the heart by absorbing the excess of heat (heart fire). The small intestine distributes the heat to the urinary bladder and to the large intestine. Thus, haemorrhoids, rectal bleeding and haematuria can all be symptoms of a heart fire. However, this is not an inflammatory condition just yet, and it should not be treated with antibiotics. The functioning of the small intestine is directly dependent on the balance of Yin and Yang within the whole body. One of the symptoms of an excess of Yin within the body can be 'foamy' diarrhoea with undigested bits of food in it. When the body is in a state of fire (excess of Yang), this will manifest itself through foul-smelling diarrhoea or diarrhoea with traces of blood. If suffering with diarrhoea, one should avoid food of the Yin nature.

## Spleen (pancreas) and stomach

The energetic peak for the spleen occurs between 9a.m. and 11a.m., and for the stomach between 7a.m. and 9a.m. (see Fig.10).

The spleen is a central organ in the Five Elements cycle. It nourishes and balances all of the other bodily organs.

The spleen – like Mother Earth – is responsible for the processes of life, rebirth and reinforcement. It transforms the energy and substance obtained from the stomach into essence and Chi, and then transfers them to the lungs, although some of this energy is also sent to the kidneys. A result of a spleen dysfunction is a bodily fluid called Yin-Ye. Yin consists of light fluids, such as tears, urine, saliva and sweat. And Ye consists of heavy fluids, such as synovial fluids, cerebrospinal fluids, gastric acids and fluids responsible for the production of blood. Ye fluids maintain life functions, renew the body and lubricate tissues and bodily organs.

The spleen is in charge of blood. It secures a sufficient quantity of blood in the veins, arteries and blood vessels. It maintains muscles and bodily organs in their original shape and state and assures the wellbeing of the whole body. It also regulates the viscosity and density of blood, strength of muscular and connective tissues, quality of subcutaneous tissue, quality of mucosa and the flexibility of joints. The spleen is responsible for the lips, eyelids, long muscles, limbs and the sense of taste.

The spleen, as a central bodily organ, keeps our emotions and mind in balance. A strong spleen enables an unobstructed flow of emotions through our mind without causing any side effects; this way the emotions become complementary to our personality and life.

The spleen represents the element of Earth. The state of balance within this particular element affects not only our concentration, consciousness and ability to analyse and classify, but also our sensitivity, intuition and openness to progress and change. A well-balanced consciousness results in such qualities as spontaneity, openness, vigilance and responsibility.

On one hand, the spleen, as a central bodily organ, supports the liver and heart, nourishes the blood and regulates its viscosity, and produces a sufficient quantity and quality of blood. On the other hand, the spleen moisturizes the lungs and kidneys and supplies them with energy Chi, essence and fluids. Within the nutrient cycle, the spleen supports the lungs (Metal), and is simultaneously supported by the energy obtained directly from the heart (Fire).

A weak and cold spleen is not able to produce essence or bodily fluids. Instead, it produces so-called pathological moisture that with time turns into mucus. This affects the nourishment of the body and the whole process of cellular metabolism. It also leads to an imbalance of Yin-Yang. The mucus, in the first instance, appears in the lungs and sinuses.

Eventually it takes over the whole body – the abdominal cavity, internal canals, bodily organs, circumventricular spaces. The excess of mucus eventually leads to a deformation of muscles and body, but also to stalling, embolism, swelling, oedema, obesity; it affects physical fitness and mobility, causes atherosclerosis and cardiovascular diseases.

One of the elements affecting the functioning of the spleen is long-lasting mental effort. This problem is very common among school children and students.

The stomach and spleen can also be adversely affected by an excess of all kinds of emotions. To the most destructive of these belong the so-called 'worrying emotions' (anxiety, apprehension, fear).

**A bad lifestyle has a profound impact on the spleen. Hard work, extensive physical effort, and a simultaneous lack of relaxation and sleep, can lead to stomach and spleen failure.** As a consequence, it can destroy the liver, heart, the circulatory system and eventually the whole body. The body can renew its substance and regenerate only during relaxation and sleep. A disregard of this very important physiological need leads to self-destruction.

In order for the spleen and the stomach to function properly, mental and emotional relaxation and reasonable physical exercise are required. But, most of all, the stomach and the spleen need warmth and an adequate quality of food. Long-lasting low body temperature can badly affect the state of both of these bodily organs. Eating the cooling kind of food can have a similar effect. **The Yin type of food of a cold and moist nature, eaten for a number of years and throughout many generations, can cause genetic mutations, degeneration and failure of not only the spleen and the stomach, but all the bodily organs.**

A malfunctioning spleen is responsible for most diseases. All health problems begin with an altered and dysfunctional spleen. However, they may also be symptoms of a bad stomach and problems with digestion and absorption.

To the symptoms of a malfunctioning spleen, that is, deficiency of Yang (cold), belong: a white discharge for women, dislocation of bodily organs, low body temperature, a feeling of heaviness, flatulence, nausea, breathlessness, spontaneous sweating during the day, swelling and obesity, allergies, susceptibility to colds, flu and tonsillitis, and heart attacks.

The spleen and the stomach are mutually interlinked. Both of them need to function properly in order to reach the state of Yin-Yang harmony. The spleen moistens the stomach with fluids, and the stomach gives the spleen dryness (energy). When the spleen is weak and does not provide the necessary quantity of juices and fluids (Yin) to the stomach, the whole balance between both organs is shaken. The stomach ends up with a 'false' excess of Yang (Fire), which results in peptic ulcers (the 'false' excess of Yang in the body is not caused by consumption of too much warm food, but an excess of Yin-type food, i.e. sour and cold food).

A malfunctioning spleen can cause imbalance of Yin-Yang. It can affect the acid-base homeostasis and lead to the so-called acidification of the body. This particular state not only weakens the whole body, but it also prevents assimilation and absorption of mineral salts and vitamins from food. Thus, every food that has a weakening effect on the spleen can consequently become an acidifier (milk, beer, juices, fruit, fresh salads, sweets, cheeses). This leads to the state of fire in the stomach, which gives a burning sensation in the stomach, causes heartburn, a bad taste in the mouth and discomfort. This condition can also be caused by strong emotions, stress and nervousness.

An imbalance between the stomach and the spleen (a weak spleen and stomach fire) is the main cause of cancer, cardiovascular diseases, diabetes and many more illnesses.

To the symptoms of a cold stomach belong: nausea, flatulence, general indigestion, headaches, a feeling of heaviness, muscular pain, a feeling of coldness, shivers, strong contractions and stomach aches.

The diet that can protect and strengthen the spleen and the stomach should be well-balanced by all the flavours, with a particular emphasis on two of them: bitter and spicy. The diet should be rich in the food characteristic of the element of Earth, always supplemented, however, with food of the other elements. Neither of the flavours should dominate the others, especially not sour or salty. What is more, the food should never be cold.

## Lungs and the large intestine

The energetic peak for the lungs occurs between 3a.m. and 5a.m., and for the large intestine between 5a.m. and 7a.m. (see Fig. 10).

Inside the lungs, Chi obtained from air merges together with Chi and essence obtained from food. This mix of energy and essence is then redistributed to the kidneys, and through blood, to the whole body. This way, by propelling Chi, the lungs simultaneously propel blood, which always follows Chi.

The lungs control certain functions of the skin; they regulate tightening and relaxing of the skin, as well as opening and closing of the pores. They are also responsible for the condition of our protective layer, the so-called Wei-Chi. This protective layer shields us against all negative influences and unexpected external factors. Its quality depends directly on the condition of our lungs.

According to the nutrient cycle and to the Five Elements Theory, the lungs are nourished and strengthened by the element of Earth (spleen). They, in turn, nourish and strengthen the element of Water (kidneys). Within the cycle of mutual checks, the lungs are in charge of the element of Wood (liver); they negate its expansive character and excessive energy and introduce stability and balance. But thanks to the element of Fire (heart), the element of Metal (lungs) becomes tamed and more flexible.

Weak lungs (deficiency of Yang and Chi) have an adverse impact on the heart and circulatory system. This manifests itself through palpitations, breathlessness and sweating.

Lung problems, like problems of other bodily organs, can be caused by a wrong diet, low body temperature and bad emotional states. All of these factors have a destructive impact on the spleen, which is responsible for the quality of the lungs. Thanks to the spleen, its fluids, essence and Chi, the lungs can ensure the proper quality of our protective layer Wei-Chi. Consequently, our resistance to colds and infections increases. Problems with the upper respiratory tract lead initially to a general weakness of the body (deficiency of Yang) and a cold spleen. Then our lungs become weaker and we end up being more susceptible to flus, catarrh, coughs, hoarseness and headaches. This is a reaction of the lungs to the deficiency of Yang.

All kinds of allergies – which have become the plague of modern life (especially for children) – are caused by deficiency of Yang (warmth and Chi in the lungs). By eating the wrong kind of food (and especially food of an overly cooling nature) we destroy our stomach, spleen and lungs. Our body reacts to it in a bad way, hence all the rashes, catarrh, breathing problems, asthma and coughs. One should remember that a weakened spleen, instead of producing beneficial fluids, starts producing mucus, which is then stored in the lungs, causing coughs.

To the symptoms of a deficiency of Yang in the lungs belong: a cough with a light discharge, catarrh, breathlessness, asthma, headaches, flu, thirst, rashes, a constant feeling of being cold, weak breath, paleness, sweating during the day, pneumonia and heart attacks.

The lungs may also be affected by the heat disease. This occurs when, due to a long-term destruction and general weakness of the spleen and the whole body, the lungs do not receive enough fluids and essence from the spleen (deficiency of Yin).

A deficiency of Yin in the lungs, combined with lung fire (heat combined with moisture), is usually the first symptom of tuberculosis or lung cancer.

If we want to eliminate catarrh, breathlessness and coughing, we have firstly to change our eating habits and start eating food that will assure a good condition of the spleen and stomach. Problems with an excess of moisture in the lungs can be treated with thyme and rosemary inhalations. In case of cold and moist lungs, one should drink bitter-flavoured herbal teas (drying properties), sweet-flavoured herbal teas (regenerating properties) and spicy herbal teas (warming properties).

The lungs are interlinked with the large intestine, which supplies them with transformed energy from the central canal. The large intestine separates all the absorbable nutrients from the indigestible matter and waste. It is dependent on the lungs, spleen and stomach, their Yang and fluids.

People who have problems with the large intestine are usually inclined to dwell on old traumas and grievances; they are sorrowful and sad. The large intestine requires proper mastication of food and physical activity. The large intestine has the ability to absorb the heat from the element of Fire; this usually leads to haemorrhoids and rectal bleeding. A malfunctioning spleen (cold spleen) which does not provide a sufficient quantity of moisture to the large intestine can cause constipation. All of the above symptoms can also occur when the body is either too cold or in the state of fire. In order for the large intestine to function well, one should take care of the spleen and the stomach, and be aware of good and bad dietary habits. For example, eating an apple in the evening for its laxative properties can cause more complications than benefit. Apple will never eliminate the source of constipation, but will actually have the opposite effect.

**Kidneys and urinary bladder**

The energetic peak for the kidneys occurs between 5p.m. and 7p.m., and for the urinary bladder between 3p.m. and 5p.m. (see Fig. 10).

The kidneys are a kind of storage receptacle of our life energy. They store the so-called 'spark of the Universe' and the energy we receive at birth from our parents.

This type of energy is non-renewable, thus it should be protected and supplemented with the energy from air and food. When the quality of our life is unsatisfying (wrong diet and lifestyle), the resources of energy and warmth simply get used up.

Each of the kidneys represents a different function. The right kidney stands for Yang (Fire) and stores our organic warmth. This is the warmth of our primal energy combined with the warmth obtained from food and air. This kidney is responsible for warming up and stimulating all bodily organs and cellular metabolism. The right kidney delivers warmth to the spleen and the stomach, both of which are leading agents in the most important process of alchemical transformation within the body – the transformation of energy and matter into Chi and the essence of life. The right kidney is the Yang root of all bodily organs.

The left kidney stands for Yin (Water). Its main function is cooling and refreshment. It stores the essence obtained from proper food and breathing, as well as the afterbirth essence. This kidney, together with the spleen and bone marrow, renews blood and bodily fluids. It has a direct effect on vaginal discharge and semen. Yin of this kidney depends directly on the functioning of the spleen, as the spleen is in fact the Yin root of all bodily organs.

The kidneys renew and nourish bones, bone marrow and the brain. They also control hair, semen and teeth. However, the strength with which teeth are attached to the gums depends on the spleen, stomach and heart.

A deficiency of Yang in the right kidney causes low body temperature and consequently weakens the body. This slows down cellular metabolism and affects the circulation of blood. One can also experience breathlessness and asthma attacks. Deficiency of Yin in the left kidney causes heat within the body (fire) and its symptoms are, for example, burning feet and hands.

To the symptoms of weak kidneys belong: grey hair, hair loss, weak bones and joints, infertility, early ageing, flaccid and dry skin, early menopause, poor eyesight and hearing problems. The kidneys stimulate excretion of faeces and urine; they are responsible for the good functioning of the reproductive organs and endocrine glands.

The kidneys can be badly affected by long-term illnesses, antibiotics, hormonal treatments, too much sex for men, tiredness and hard physical work, stress and coldness.

The wrong kind of food can only augment the susceptibility of the body to these sorts of influence. By wrong food, in this case, we mean food with cooling properties (sour, raw and cold food). This kind of food is not able to supplement our requirements for Yang.

The kidneys are the nest of our life energy. They are our vitality engine. They stimulate our creativity and curiosity. Thanks to the kidneys, we have the will and eagerness for living. Well-functioning kidneys can provide the energy to do things, to enjoy life, to be creative and eager to discover new things. A deficiency of Yang in the kidneys can lead to depression, reclusiveness, general stiffness, sadness, cynicism, loss of the will for living. For example, suicidal thoughts and actions are all symptoms of a deficiency of Yang in the kidneys.

Bad eating habits can seriously affect our emotional state and health. For example, eating too much pork, ham and sausages, herrings and salty food, all of which are of a very strong Yin nature and belong to the element of Water, can result in the above-mentioned problems. This type of food leads to a deficiency of Yang in the kidneys and, ultimately, to their destruction. Then we become susceptible to depression and energetic blockages, both of which we often try to overcome by drinking alcohol. This situation is one of the causes of alcoholism within society. To strengthen the kidneys one should eat more freshwater fish, which are a great source of nutrients beneficial to the kidneys.

In order to eliminate health problems and emotional imbalance, one should take into consideration the nature of the food products and especially avoid large quantities of meals of the Yin nature.

The kidneys are interlinked with the urinary bladder. The urinary bladder supplies the kidneys with the energy from the central canal. Problems with the kidneys can cause problems with the urinary bladder and vice versa. The urinary bladder also has a close energetic relationship with the small intestine. They exchange with one another the excess of Yin and Yang. For example, the urinary bladder protects the small intestine by reducing the excess of heat in the small intestine. On the other hand, the small intestine does the same for the heart by reducing its Fire. The latter usually manifests itself as haematuria. However, this is still not a state of inflammation.

Fig. 9. Interactions between bodily organs.

## Energetic peaks and lows of bodily organs and their meridians

Apart from the inner relationships and interdependences between bodily organs (control cycle and nutrient cycle) there also occur energetic relationships between the meridians of particular bodily organs. The meridians are the canals of the so-called enlivening energy. They are located inside and outside of the body. There are 12 meridians ascribed to 12 different bodily organs. In acupuncture or acupressure these canals enable transfer of energy between particular bodily organs, which helps to eliminate energetic stalls and blockages. In case of a deficiency of energy within the body, one should avoid acupuncture.

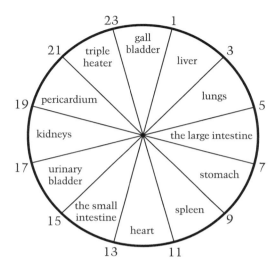

Fig. 10. Biological clock.

The flow of energy inside the meridians is continuous and reaches its peaks and lows at different times of the day and night. During these peaks and lows, particular bodily organs reveal their excesses and deficiencies, which result in specific symptoms. For example, a complete lack of appetite in the morning indicates problems with a cold and weakened spleen and stomach. Insomnia, on the other hand, can be a symptom of a hot liver and heart. Severe coughs, breathlessness or heartaches early in the morning indicate problems with weakened lungs and heart. Craving sweets at night indicates a deficiency of Yin in the liver. Early-morning tiredness and sleepiness signal a weakened spleen. Midday sleepiness, on the other hand, is a symptom of a weakened liver. These are examples of Yin-Yang imbalance inside the bodily organs.

# FACTORS AFFECTING THE BALANCE OF YIN-YANG WITHIN THE BODY

## Flavours

Nature has equipped us with different senses, so we can assess and choose what is good for us and reject all that is bad. The most important senses in the process of food preparation, and nutrition overall, are the senses of taste, smell and sight.

Eyes enable us to familiarize ourselves with and evaluate the environment. The sense of smell alerts us to what is beneficial or harmful, pleasant or unpleasant to us. On the other hand, the sense of taste enables us to choose the food that is best for our system.

The condition of our senses depends on our health. In other words, they can respond to external stimuli in the correct way or quite the contrary – in a way that can feed us with all the wrong information. This can be quite dangerous to our health and is usually a symptom of certain problems within our body.

A good quality of eyesight is dependent on a well-functioning liver. The sense of smell, on the other hand, is dependent on the lungs and the sense of taste on the spleen and pancreas. To fully benefit from the sense of taste, one should eat food that is well balanced with all the Five Flavours. Only then can the sense of taste function properly and prevent us from receiving false information.

There are five basic flavours: sour, bitter, sweet, spicy and salty. In order for our body to function properly we need all of them. Each one plays a prescribed role. Positive results, however, can only be achieved when each of these flavours is accompanied by the other four. When this occurs, they then work in balance.

Sour and salty belong to Yin flavours. Bitter, sweet and spicy are Yang flavours; however, cold or raw food of these particular flavours is always Yin, except for hot-flavoured spices and garlic, onion and leeks, which are, in fact, always warming and stimulating.

Fig. 11. Order of flavours

## Sour flavour – the element of Wood

The sour flavour is of the Yin nature; it is cooling and refreshing. It has tightening properties, often leading to contractions. It is indispensable to maintaining a well-functioning liver and its metabolism. It regulates the liver's function of transporting energy. When a diet lacks the sour flavour, certain disruptions in energy circulation may occur, especially within the element of Earth (stomach, spleen). This manifests itself through indigestion, flatulence, nausea, vomiting, the feeling of a full stomach and headaches. In this case, we are dealing with the energy travelling mainly upwards. The quantity of sour-flavoured food should be well balanced; this flavour should be never dominant. All food belonging to the element of Wood must also be very carefully balanced with the other four flavours.

On the other hand, an excess of the sour flavour can destroy the Yang of the liver, spleen and stomach. This can lead to stalling of the energy flow and weakening of the blood circulation. The intensity of cellular nutrition and removal of toxins can also drop significantly. This leads to stagnation, stalling, high blood pressure, problems with metabolism and women's illnesses. The tightening and slowing-down properties of this flavour can at the same time lead to a low temperature in the whole body. Then the liver is not being supplied with enough blood and starts contracting; this is often very strong and painful (the so-called liver wind). It is quite a common condition in small children, especially after eating sour fruit, such as strawberries. In this situation, sweet and spicy flavours are very helpful.

**One should avoid eating sour food in the evening.** It can disturb regeneration of the liver, which usually happens during its energetic peak between 1a.m. and 3a.m. It could also badly affect the spleen and the stomach, when between 7p.m. and 11p.m. they reach their energetic lows. That is why it is not advisable to eat wheat bread, fresh salad, yogurt, fruit, sour soup or pasta with a sour sauce for supper. Supper should consist of sweet and warming meals (but with no addition of sugar). This also applies to summer meals, and especially to those eaten after swimming in the sea or a lake.

The sour flavour should be avoided in the diet of babies or children. It is only allowed as a balancing flavour element. Fruit yogurts, fruit juices and fruit (especially citruses) and pickled gherkins are good for people with a fully formed and mature liver, but the tightening and contracting properties of the sour flavour prevent a proper development of bodily organs in a young person.

Cravings for sour food indicate that there is a problem with a weakened liver (deficiency of Yang and Yin). Women who eat lemons or other sour fruit during pregnancy give birth to children susceptible to allergies and various health problems. By satisfying cravings for sour food one only weakens one's liver and spleen even more. In this case, one should instead eat cooked food, mostly sweet (the element of Earth) and warming.

The excess of sour flavour, and especially when one is already dealing with a weakened liver, also leads to eye problems and emotional problems. Sour flavour is not advisable when one suffers from allergies, circulation diseases, blood clots, paralysis, high blood pressure, pre-heart attack conditions, indigestion, obesity, diabetes, psoriasis, gout, arthritis, rheumatism, gallstones, kidney stones, fibroids, tumours, swelling, dislocation of bodily organs, migraines and cancer. In all these cases, sour flavour should be used only as a balancing flavour element.

We should also not overestimate the benefits of vitamin C in medical and preventive treatments. It affects our system in a similar way to the sour flavour – with all the same consequences. We only need small quantities of vitamin C to regulate the liver. Excess of vitamin C affects the liver, spleen and kidneys as much as the excess of sour flavour.

Stress, in conjunction with a long-term diet that weakens the stomach and the spleen and leads to Yin deficiency (frozen food, tinned food, too much meat, too many sweets), can cause liver and heart fire. It can also result in various oral problems, such as bleeding gums and periodontitis. In such cases, adding more sour flavour to the diet can be very helpful, but only over a short period of time. For example, overdosing vitamin C can only make the situation worse. Once the above-mentioned symptoms have been sorted out, one should go back to the well-balanced diet.

Sour flavour is also helpful in hepatitis. However, one should avoid eating too much sour food (lemons, chicken, yogurt, white cheese, white bread) over a long period of time, as in the end it can destroy not only the liver but also the spleen and the lungs. A special wheat diet, which usually lasts twelve days and is supported by drinking wheat beer or parsley tea, can effectively level out any irregularities (liver fire and heart fire).

The sour flavour is associated not only with lemons and sour fruit but also with chicken, sauerkraut, pickled gherkins, white cheese, yogurt, white bread and parsley. All of these products should always be accompanied by those of a spicy or bitter flavour. For example, yogurt should be served with buckwheat, chicken with ginger, turmeric and garlic, parsley should be added to broths and sauerkraut should be balanced out with carrot, onion, juniper berry and thyme.

## Bitter flavour – the element of Fire

The bitter-warm flavour is of the Yang nature (warming). This flavour has dispersing, stimulating and drying-up properties.

The bitter-cold flavour is of the Yin nature (drying and cooling). This flavour has cooling properties which activate through dispersion.

The bitter-warm flavour is associated with energy, movement and warmth. It stimulates blood circulation, maintains heartbeat and strengthens the spleen, stomach, lungs, large intestine, kidneys and urinary bladder. It also eliminates cold moisture and white mucus. This flavour is indispensable in our climate in order to propel the energy and to dry out the moisture accumulated from eating the cooling types of food, such as dairy, meat and fruit.

The bitter flavour (marjoram, thyme, turmeric, rosemary, tarragon, mugwort) is necessary to keep the balance in the all-year diet, and especially in preparation of meat and vegetable–meat meals. It prevents stagnation and stalling.

Buckwheat and lamb (both bitter flavoured) belong to products of a highly warming nature. They are indispensable in the reconstruction of Yang and the Yin substance. Boiled natural coffee has similar properties; it strengthens blood circulation and spleen, keeps the lungs dry and warms up the kidneys. In contrast, brewed coffee is unbalanced; it stimulates the nervous system but it does not have the same warming effect on the body. In the end, this can result in a quite unpleasant sensation. The bitter-warm flavour used in excess can damage the heart, stomach and lungs (large quantities of coffee). It also should not be applied in excess when dealing with the 'heat' diseases.

The bitter-cold flavour has strongly cooling properties. It is used as a treatment for liver fire (gentiana, mugwort), large intestine fire (rheum) and heart fire (beer). It also helps to dry the hot moisture in the lungs. Green tea also has strongly cooling properties and helps to eliminate the hot moisture from the gall bladder (hence its popularity in China). Of similar properties is black tea; it is cooling, drying and diuretic. It is helpful in the case of diarrhoea and as a compress for burns. The bitter-cold flavour should be applied carefully when dealing with children and people suffering from general weakness, low body temperature and deficiency of bodily fluids. Those prone to heart attacks, circulatory diseases and strokes (paralysis) should avoid black tea as well.

## Sweet flavour – the element of Earth

The sweet flavour has warming properties and the sweet-cold flavour has refreshing properties. The sweet flavour represents outer movement; it strengthens, maintains balance and nourishes.

The notion of 'sweet' in this case stands for natural sweetness, which should not be identified with sugar. For example, the sweetness of Earth can be extracted when chewing cereal. Sweet is the foundation of all culinary processes, which should result in creating food that could become the Earth to all bodily organs.

This flavour plays a nourishing, building and strengthening role during the growing-up period. Thus, it should become a dominant element of the diet for babies, children and youth. This flavour in particular is responsible for the proper growth of the body. However, in order to maintain continuous regeneration and reconstruction of the substance within the body, this flavour should be present also in the diet of adults. Sweet flavour is indispensable when it comes to dealing with deficiency of blood and Yin within the body (all of the symptoms of fire and heat). It also strengthens concentration and clarity of thought.

However, excess of the sweet flavour can significantly weaken the spleen and damage the kidneys. Too much sweet-flavoured food, such as potatoes, butter, eggs, carrots and honey, can lead to imbalance within the element of Earth, stalling of the internal fluids and destruction of the element of Water.

The sweet-cold flavour has cooling and refreshing properties. It strengthens Yin, but can be used only during the summer, when we should eat all ripe and sweet fruit.

To the sweet-flavoured foods belong soups, mostly those based on stock obtained from beef, calf or turkey bones, with the addition of carrots, parsnips, parsley root, celeriac, leeks, onion and garlic, greens or tomatoes, turmeric, thyme and hot spices. Of similar character are meat and vegetable stews; however, they should always be well balanced with all the Five Flavours. Meals based merely on vegetables, representing the element of Earth or the element of Metal, can cause flatulence and headaches, as they simply lack the balance. However, by adding the other three flavours we can make them easier to assimilate. The sweet (warming) flavour is especially important in evening meals for it strengthens the stomach and the spleen during their energetic lows, which occur between 7p.m. and 11p.m.

The common source of the sweet flavour in our daily diet is sugar (sweets, cakes, chocolates). But this is not a natural flavour, as sugar is an artificially extracted substance. It has, in fact, a cooling and destructive effect on our body; it stimulates production of mucus, acidifies the body, and in consequence weakens the immune system. If we do decide from time to time to indulge in sugar and sweets, let's try not to lose control over it or just prepare ourselves to bear the consequences of such overindulgence.

## Spicy flavour – the element of Metal

The spicy-hot flavour has 'unlocking', dispersing and stimulating properties.

The spicy-cold flavour unlocks and stimulates.

The spicy-hot flavour activates the flow of energy Chi and blood. It creates motion, and motion produces warmth. It eliminates indigestion, nausea, flatulence (pepper vodka, ginger tea). It also stimulates blood circulation, metabolism, regulates peristalsis of the intestines, eliminates muscular contractions (ginger) and helps in getting rid of coldness and moisture (garlic, onion, leeks). This flavour is indispensable when fighting low body temperature (grog, tea with rum, coffee with ginger). It loosens and stimulates all that is tightened, contracted and stiffened or under pressure. It also helps digestion.

The spicy-hot flavour is very important in our diet. Because of the climate we live in, we need substantial kinds of food that are rich in meat and fat. The spicy flavour enables the proper usage and distribution of energy and substance. Deficiency of this particular flavour leads to stagnation, accumulation of moisture, bad metabolism, a feeling of heaviness and obesity.

The spicy flavour represents motion and spreading out. Thus, active people (for example – sportsmen) do not need as much of this flavour as people leading a sedentary lifestyle.

However, the spicy-hot flavour, when unaccompanied by other flavours, can be rather harmful for the lungs, liver and kidneys. It should be avoided in large quantities especially when dealing with 'heat' diseases (deficiency of Yin). It helps to disperse the coldness within the element of Earth (stomach, spleen) and propels the energy within the element of Wood (liver).

The spicy-cold flavour (peppermint) helps to control liver fire. But used in excess, it can damage the liver and also has a very bad influence on the eyes.

## Salty flavour – the element of Water

The salty flavour is of a cooling nature. It creates motion inwardly and downwardly. It has a toning character and maintains the existing balance as well as its lack. Together with the other flavours, it strengthens, replenishes, nourishes, but also eliminates all kind of deficiencies. Also, in conjunction with the other flavours, it accelerates assimilation of food and metabolism, improves the general health condition and immunity. It helps to rebuild the substance –

blood and internal fluids (Yin). For example, beans, with the addition of the sour flavour (tomatoes or parsley), with turmeric and thyme, sweet vegetables, some beef, some rice, garlic, onion and ginger, enable the appropriate level of energy Chi and substance (blood, internal fluids) to be maintained. It nourishes the kidneys, and strengthens the liver and spleen. We should cook fish and pork in a similar way, for they also require both the spicy and the bitter flavour.

The salty flavour is associated with salt. Used in excess, it acquires cooling properties and can cause stiffness, the withholding of moisture and fluids and stalling of blood. Salt, beans, soya beans, fish, pork – all of these food products eaten in excess and without the addition of the other flavours (and especially without bitter and spicy) can cause arthritic and rheumatic pains and also damage the kidneys, heart and intestines and disrupt the blood circulation. Excess of the salty flavour (pork, ham and sausages) results in a stiffened body with hardly any energy and blood flow, problems with metabolism and obesity and also depression. One can overcome this difficult situation by adding appropriate spices and matching together appropriate food products. But under no condition should one use the sour and the bitter-cold flavours in this particular situation. The salty flavour should always be used in proportion to the other flavours. Otherwise, it can ruin our health.

However, if our body needs cooling or inner moistening, then the salty flavour (beans, fish and pork) is very much recommended. It prevents excessive sweating. That is why, in countries with a hot climate, the basic diet consists of beans, soya beans, pork and fish. But it is important to mention that all this is cooked with the addition of many spices and balancing elements that make the food light, easy to assimilate and good for the body.

## Climates

Many illnesses can arise as a result of external factors. The five seasons, or the so-called climates, are such factors, and these are directly interlinked with the Five Elements Theory. Following the Five Elements Theory can be beneficial to our health. Once we understand the impact of external factors on our body, we can prevent many diseases and health problems.

So, for example, in winter, in order to prevent excessive cooling of the body, we should dress appropriately, taking into account the external weather conditions. Similarly, in the summer, we should wear light clothes to lower our body temperature. These rules are especially important for babies and children. We should also adapt to the changes in Nature by applying different seasonal diets and be especially careful when including fruit, fresh salads, ice cream and cold drinks in our daily diet.

In order to protect our health effectively, we should act reasonably and observe Nature carefully. All of the widely advertised new diets and lifestyles should be treated with a dose of scepticism. In the long run, all these novelties can have a detrimental effect on our body, for they are not usually adapted to our climatic and dietary needs.

To live against the rules of Nature means to expose our body to the harmful influence of external factors, such as wind, heat, humidity or cold air, which consequently leads to an imbalance within our body and many health problems.

A healthy person should be able to cope with all the inconveniences caused by changes in the weather and consciously react to the needs of their own body.

Through observation of seasonal change, the surrounding environment and the energy within it, we can set our life in a mode of cyclical behaviours and preferences. For example, in autumn, when the trees lose their leaves and start storing the essence in order to survive the winter, we should replace any cooling and raw food with food of warming and strengthening properties.

In autumn, one should get rid of all moisture and coldness accumulated during the summer (cooling drinks, ice cream, fruit and cold swims). If we neglect this, it will manifest itself in late autumn and winter through all sorts of health problems. Autumn is not a good time to start a starvation diet.

The winter period is energetically imbalanced (excess of Yin). Therefore, we should calm ourselves and make sure we do not lose too much of our body temperature. We can do this by eating warm and energetic food and dressing according to the weather conditions. Starvation diets are strictly forbidden in winter time.

The spring period, when leaves appear on the trees, is the most suitable for all sorts of changes and detox diets. We can gradually start introducing food of a refreshing nature, fresh and green vegetables, and at the same time we should cut down on meat. For detox enthusiasts, spring is the most appropriate period to implement a starvation diet.

Summer is very important in terms of strengthening the body. This not only means cooling the body, but also gathering and accumulating enough nutrients to last throughout autumn and winter and to make our body strong and resistant to any health problems. However, we should not interpret this as encouragement to overeat fruit, fresh salads and to drink large quantities of fruit juices.

## Wind

The wind is associated with spring (the element of Wood) and has a direct influence on the liver. The notion of 'wind' in this case refers not only to a meteorological phenomenon but to all sorts of air movements, such as, for example, the blowing of the wind through an open car window, air movement caused by an electric fan or simply a draught.

The wind has an expansive, piercing and irritating effect on the body. It is often combined with other external phenomena, such as humidity of air, dryness, cold and hot weather.

The biggest impact of the wind is on the upper body: the chest, neck and head. Exposure to wind can cause headaches, conjunctivitis, skin irritation, muscular contractions and colds. All these are symptoms of a weakened liver, a general imbalance within the body and deficiency of Chi.

## Heat

Heat is associated with summer (the element of Fire) and has a direct influence on the heart. As in the case of the wind, the notion of 'heat' is much broader than just a meteorological phenomenon. It can refer to all sorts of physical experiences, such as a visit to a sauna, a hot bath or simply wearing too many layers of clothing. In our climatic zone, summers are fairly mild. Nevertheless, in order to prevent unnecessary weakness, tiredness, sweating or excessive thirst, one should know how to deal with the effects of heat. One crucial rule is to avoid cold drinks, ice cream and too much fruit. In this case, cooling drinks and cold food can only cause tiredness, thirst, sweating, swelling and headaches. By eating too much food of a cooling nature we can weaken the spleen, kidneys and heart.

**Excessive cooling of the body during hot days is in fact the cause of many diseases in developed countries**.

Why should we not quench our thirst by drinking cold drinks? The surrounding heat stimulates blood circulation and metabolism. And as we have already seen, the balance between Yin and Yang within our body should always be maintained. Thus, once our Yang has risen, we should also raise our internal Yin. However, Yin is totally dependent on the condition of the spleen, which produces all the required internal moisture and hydrates the body from within. By drinking cold drinks we automatically weaken the spleen and simultaneously dry out our body, as the spleen is unable to produce enough internal fluids. By drinking cold drinks or eating ice cream and fruit, we start feeling even more thirsty and dry and we sweat more. All cooling products should be eaten in moderation. Cold drinks will not prevent the body from drying out and thirst.

To quench our thirst, we should drink warm and hot drinks, mostly of a bitter taste. An excellent drink in this case is boiled chicory coffee or boiled natural coffee. Workers who carry out hard manual work especially should drink cooled bitter drinks (natural and chicory coffee). In the old days, popular drinks among harvesters were mugwort tea and sour milk, both of which are good for sunstroke prevention. The bitter taste protects the heart and strengthens the spleen, enabling the latter to produce a sufficient amount of internal bodily fluids. On the other hand, black and green teas are not recommended, for they have drying-out properties.

A sauna is beneficial only to those in good health. It relaxes and improves the mood. Those who eat exclusively food of the Yin nature and suffer from an inner imbalance (deficiency of Yang), and those who are easily excitable and aggressive and suffer from the so-called inner fire, should be very careful about using saunas. In both these cases, using a sauna can cause heart and circulatory problems. The same rules apply to hot baths.

## Humidity/Dampness

Humidity is associated with late summer. As an external factor, it has a direct impact on the spleen and lungs. Its influence is especially disadvantageous when combined with food of a cooling and moist nature (sugar, milk, fruit).

Dampness within a living space also has a bad effect on health. Long-term exposure to dampness can not only cause tuberculosis and other lung diseases, but also malaria; combined with exposure to cold and wind, it can lead to rheumatism. In order to protect oneself from the effects of dampness (or humidity), cold, moist, raw, sour and salty food should be eaten in moderation. On the other hand, it is advisable to ingest food of a warming nature with the addition of a bitter and hot flavour.

## Dryness

Dryness as a meteorological phenomenon is associated with autumn. It has a direct impact on the lungs and usually causes dry coughs. In our climatic zone, dryness rarely affects people. It is associated more with a desert climate. However, dryness can also be experienced in closed spaces (at home), and especially during cold winters. As we know, there is no moisture in the air below 0 °C. Thus, when ventilating a room in winter we should control and balance the moisture of the air. As to the winter diet, we should mostly eat warm and fattening food of a sweet flavour (but no sugar). We should strictly avoid fruit, fresh salads and cold drinks, as they are not suitable to balance the surrounding dryness.

## Cold

Cold is associated with winter and has a direct impact on the kidneys, and especially the right one. Long-term exposure to cold exhausts our Yang and enables Yin to dominate within our body. Cold slows down metabolism and blood circulation; the whole body stiffens, the muscles tighten and shrink. This leads to depression, apathy and lethargy, and as a result we become susceptible to illnesses and stress. In order to avoid cold we should dress properly and eat warming food.

## Calendar of activity of the body organs

The activity of the bodily organs changes cyclically throughout the year in accordance with the seasonal change (see Fig. 12). For example, the liver is mostly active in spring, the heart in summer, the lungs in autumn and the kidneys in winter.

The stomach and the spleen are active during late summer. This particular season keeps all four seasons in balance and strengthens them accordingly. In the calendar of the activity of our bodily organs, late summer represents the Centre and, as presented in the chart below, it separates the seasons with periods that are 18 days long. During these periods, the spleen and the stomach reach the peak of their activity.

Fig. 12. Calendar of activity of the body organs.

Each season lasts 72 days. In the middle of each falls a solar solstice or equinox: spring equinox is on the 22nd of March (liver), summer solstice on the 22nd of June (heart), autumn equinox on the 22nd of September (lungs), and winter solstice on the 22nd of December (kidneys). Between the seasons there is always a period that is 18 days long, the so-called Dojo (spleen).

The calendar indicates optimal moments suitable for strengthening particular bodily organs. These are also the moments of the most intense activity of particular bodily organs. Thus, for example, in winter we should take care of the kidneys and strengthen them with food from the elements of Fire and

Earth (avoid food from the element of Water). In the summer, on the other hand, we should strengthen the heart with food from the elements of Water and Wood. In spring we should strengthen the liver with food from the elements of Wood, Water and Earth, and in autumn strengthen the lungs with food from the elements of Metal, Fire and Earth.

If any of the bodily organs malfunctions during the period of its peak of activity, it may be a symptom of a Yin-Yang imbalance within this particular organ. In other words, the organ is suffering from deficiency of Yin.

## Emotions

Each person is born with a certain behavioural code, a pattern of emotional predispositions. Thanks to this pattern, one is able to evolve mentally and spiritually throughout life. However, the direction of such transformation depends on the willingness and determination of the individual.

Each personality is dominated by one particular element, but always with a larger or lesser influence of the other four elements. It is simply impossible to acquire the characteristics of Wood only or only the characteristics of Water. If that was the case, it would be very difficult to live and co-exist.

Emotions identified with particular elements pass through our life like day and night or sun and rain. Examples of such emotions include happiness and sadness, tears and laughter, aggression and tolerance, grief and openness, fear and courage. If one of these emotions dominates our mind, it can destroy a particular bodily organ and, consequently, the whole body. In order to decide about our own health and our quality of life, it is inevitable that we have to be conscious of our own character and personality.

The Five Elements Theory provides us with knowledge about our emotions; it enables us to identify the causes of certain emotions and, if necessary, helps us to calm and neutralize them.

Within the Five Elements there are two pairs of elements that are direct opposites of one another, yet balance out (see Fig. 12). They are: Water (winter) and Fire (summer), and Wood (spring) and Metal (autumn). Earth (late summer) is an axis, which keeps in balance all cyclically transforming energies, processes and emotions, both within Nature and in the human body. Identifying various behavioural characteristics associated with a particular element, we should always look at the dependencies within the scheme of the control cycle (see Fig. 6). For example, if we identify ourselves with the element of Wood (with all its characteristics), we should consciously, through self-discipline, adopt characteristics of the element of Metal.

And so, intolerance and anger should be balanced with altruism and compassion. We can also balance negative emotions with positive ones belonging to the same element. For example, anger and aggression can be balanced with patience and tolerance. This kind of conscious work on oneself leads to the creation of one's own existence. This is the way of Tao, where in order to gain strength and enrich oneself, one uses all of the life elements.

**The element of Wood** (liver) is associated with activity and movement. This element is most active in spring. For the Wood type of personality, characteristics associated with this element include cleverness, vitality, independence, relying on oneself and a desire for transformation and change.

The most typical emotion associated with the liver is anger. This emotion is of a strong Yang nature; it moves the energy up and down and burns internal fluids. Anger can lead to an instability of the mind.

The positive characteristics of the Wood type of personality are: hard working, cleverness, self-confidence, determination, problem-solving skills, leadership and organizational skills, and tolerance.

The negative characteristics of the Wood type of personality include: aggression, nervousness, intolerance, relentlessness, fanaticism, tyranny, hostility, poor judgement, a quarrelsome nature, unpredictability and selfishness.

Emotions typical of the element of Wood should be balanced with emotions from the elements of Metal and Earth. When there is deficiency of Yin in the liver (Fire), we become more quick-tempered, aggressive and angry. On the other hand, when there is deficiency of Yang (cold), we become more indecisive, irritable and lenient.

**The element of Fire** (heart) is most powerful in the summer; it fills us up, makes us excitable and gives us a feeling of strength and power. Fire is warm and active. It represents awakening, wisdom, intuition and compassion.

One of the most characteristic emotions of the element of Fire is joy. It is a typical emotion of Yang, which directly affects the heart. If it comes from within, from a natural state of mind and not from external factors, then our body is in a state of balance. On the other hand, if joy is experienced too often and for too long a period of time, and is caused by external factors, then it can damage the heart and the whole body; we are then unable to concentrate and relax.

The positive characteristics of the element of Fire are: charisma, articulation, responsibility, optimism, compassion, enthusiasm, ability for sacrifice, vigilance. The negative characteristics of the element of Fire include: sentimentality, insatiability, anxiety, over-sensitivity, carelessness, absent-mindedness, talkativeness, hysteria, and infantile laughter.

The positive characteristics of the element of Fire occur only when there is a state of peace and clarity of mind (subconscious), chastity of the heart and a well-balanced consciousness. One should remember that the liver represents the subconscious, the heart represents the mind and the spleen represents consciousness. Thus, the condition of our bodily organs has a direct impact on our state of mind, and vice versa – our state of mind can affect the functioning of our bodily organs.

The dominant characteristics of the element of Fire (both negative and positive) should be balanced with the characteristics from the elements of Water and Metal, but mostly as a means of introducing balance to our consciousness.

Deficiency of Yin in the heart (Fire) manifests itself through such characteristics as: carelessness, a talkative nature, excitement and laughter. When there is deficiency of Yang (cold), one becomes more silent, fearful and bewildered.

**The element of Earth** (spleen) is most active during the late summer, when all has ripened and been accomplished. The element of Earth brings stability and physical and mental balance; it defines our place in life. The Earth is like a mother to us. It gives birth to us and feeds us. It protects, averts conflicts, strengthens, creates a friendly environment for living and gives us security. Good quality of the element of Earth enables proper concentration and attentiveness.

A very characteristic emotion for the element of Earth is excessive and obsessive thinking, the so-called worrying state. Such a state of mind blocks the flow of energy and destroys the spleen.

Some of the positive characteristics of the element of Earth are: caring, sociability, compassion, sensibility, self-control and generosity.

Negative characteristics of the element of Earth comprise: over-protectiveness, interfering in the matters of others, concern, worrying, feeling blue, apathy, gloominess and capriciousness.

People who lack a balance within the element of Earth are usually conformist; they act and think in accordance with commonly accepted norms and rules and are resistant to all that is new or different.

The dominant characteristics of the element of Earth (negative and positive) should be balanced with the characteristics from the elements of Water and Wood.

An excess of the element of Earth leads to impudence, over-protectiveness and constant interfering in the matters of others. A deficiency of Yang within this element (cold) leads to a lack of self-confidence, capriciousness and constant worrying.

**The element of Metal** (lungs) is most active in autumn – the time of concentration and separation. Autumn is a good time for a separation of all that is necessary from all that is useless. It is also the time of stocking up goods for winter.

The typical emotion for the element of Metal is sadness. It affects the lungs, moving the energy down, and causing tiredness and stooping. Thus, sadness affects the whole posture of the body.

Positive characteristics of the element of Metal include: conscientiousness, attention to detail, discipline, neatness, self-control, tolerance, assertiveness and the ability to stop brooding over the past or the future.

Some of the negative characteristics of the element of Metal are: excessive perfectionism, prejudice, indifference, imperturbability and dogmatism.

When one's personality is dominated by the element of Metal, one shows a tendency to hesitate and constantly analyse what is good or what is bad. Such people also have a tendency to criticize and make judgements about other people. In order to make the element of Metal more flexible, one should warm it up with the element of Fire and neutralize it with the element of Wood.

Deficiency of Yin in the element of Metal (Fire) manifests itself through harshness, indifference and coldness, and deficiency of Yang (cold) through apathy, sloppiness and scrupulousness.

**The element of Water** (kidneys) is most active in winter. It is responsible for the kidneys – the source of our vitality. The element of Water represents free and creative work, willpower and an eagerness to discover oneself as well as the surrounding world.

The most destructive emotion of this element is fear (Yin); it moves the energy down. Long-lasting fear can lead to depression. Some of the positive characteristics of the element of Water are common sense, reasoning, curiosity, humbleness and fearlessness.

Some negative characteristics of the element of Water are greediness, cynicism, reclusiveness, suspiciousness, a lack of tact, being critical, a susceptibility to fears and phobias, avarice and pessimism.

It would be best to merge the powers and creativity of Water with the openness and expressiveness of Fire, and the compassion and gentleness of Earth.

A deficiency of Yin in the kidneys (Fire) is characteristic of people who are excessively eccentric, excessively demanding, greedy and with excessive bravado.

On the other hand, a deficiency of Yang (cold) in the kidneys leads to depression, suicidal thoughts, phobias and a sarcastic and distrustful disposition.

**Remember:**

- Wood (liver) = determination, anger and patience
- Fire (heart) = passion, infantile laughter and joy
- Earth (spleen) = generosity, obsessiveness and concentration
- Metal (lungs) = discipline, sadness and altruism
- Water (kidneys) = will, fear and bravura.

Generally, we are unaware of the type of personality we represent. We feel neurotic, chaotic, lost and nervous, and yet we think that this is normal, that this is all a mere derivative of our own character or certain external factors.

We should acknowledge that often the way we behave can in fact be dictated by the state of our bodily organs.

By implementing a proper kind of diet, we can significantly improve the wellbeing of our body both in a physical and emotional sense. Excessive excitability, aggression (particularly for children), problems with sleep, irritability, nervousness, excessive susceptibility to stress, depression – all of these emotional states can be eliminated relatively quickly thanks to a well-balanced diet. This will help us to reach emotional equilibrium and feel satisfaction from the process of self-creation.

## Colours

According to the Five Elements Theory, each of the elements is represented by one particular colour, e.g. Fire – red, Earth – yellow, Metal – white, Water – blue, Wood – green.

Colours, as well as tastes, climates and emotions, have an immense impact on the balance of Yin-Yang. Each of the colours radiates a special kind of energy, which weakens, stimulates or balances our life energy.

A disregard of the meaning of colours in our life can lead to a general imbalance within our system and all sorts of emotional issues.

The importance of colours in our life is supported by the theory of human chakras. Chakras are vortices of energy. They correspond to seven basic colours: red, orange, yellow, green, blue, indigo and purple. We can distinguish two types of chakra: lower chakras and upper chakras. If the lower chakras are filled with such colours as red, orange and yellow, then automatically the upper chakras will be filled with the other four colours: green, blue, indigo and purple.

I would like to remind you at this point that our physicality has its equivalent in the so-called astral body (emotions). The astral body constitutes our consciousness. It is also responsible for the creation of our mental body (subconscious). And it is our mental body that has a direct impact on the Supreme Self, or in other words – the Overmind.

How then can we reach the state of true spirituality? There is only one way – through our physicality. Only by taking care of our physicality and by staying in constant touch with the Earth can we reach the state of healthy consciousness and, consequently, the state of true spirituality. Opting for a shorter and quicker way, which is very popular nowadays, can be extremely dangerous. It only shows the lack of humility in modern man. Extreme experiences, which are thought by many to be spiritually charged, are pure illusion. Contact with spirituality should remind one more of a gentle gust of wind, not a gale. We have been given life in order to experience its whole physical aspect with all respect and joy, and then to seek spiritual experience.

According to the Five Elements Theory, the most important colours in human life are red (Fire) and yellow (Earth). The energy of these two colours has an influence on the state of our physicality, physiological and regenerative processes and on the state of our emotional balance.

Red signifies the element of Fire. Its energy ensures proper blood circulation and a sufficient quantity of Yang in each of the bodily organs. The energy of this colour is equivalent to the energy of our physical life, which is a carrier of our spirit. Thanks to the influence of red we can eliminate a low body temperature and weakness; we can increase our immunity to external factors and reach mental balance.

Yellow signifies the element of Earth. The energy of this colour has an influence on our digestion and the absorption of nutrients, as well as on the quantity of bodily fluids; it ensures a balance of Yin within the whole body. Yellow is the most neutral of all colours. Its energy improves our consciousness and emotional state. Both yellow and red belong to warm colours. Thus, they have a warming effect on the body.

White, green and blue signify the cold colours. Too much of these colours in the surrounding environment can cause an imbalance and lowering of the level of life energy. For example, too much of the colour white badly affects the elements of Fire and Metal. On the other hand, too much blue does the same to the elements of Water and Fire, and too much green has a destructive effect on the elements of Fire, Earth, Metal and Water. The green of plants is needed only during the summer to balance the Yang of the Sun. We do not need this colour in winter; in fact, in our climate it can cause more damage than good to our health condition.

Red is not suitable for people with an excess of 'false' Yang (Fire). This problem affects mainly the liver, heart and lungs. I need to remind you at this point that, in our climate, the state of fire within the body is not caused by too much heat or red colour, but by excessive cooling and deficiency of Yang (a malfunctioning spleen). In the situation of liver or heart fire, such cold colours as white, blue and green can only bring a short-lasting calming effect, after which one may experience certain health problems. The state of fire within the body is characteristic of adults. For them, the most suitable colour in this case is yellow. The energy of yellow can improve the functioning of the spleen and stomach and lead to Yin-Yang balance (internal fluids) and level out our emotional state.

It is a misconception that hyperactivity disorder and aggression amongst children, the young and adults are always caused by the state of fire within the body or an overexposure to the colour red. Another misconception is that green has healing properties in such cases. That is not true.

Green can only temporarily ease the symptoms of aggression or hyperactivity, but eventually it destabilizes the emotional state even more. The emotional imbalance in children, the young and adults is actually caused by a shortage of red and yellow, which means that together they cause an imbalance within the elements of Earth and Fire. Green causes typical cooling symptoms. Thus, all of the cold colours (white, blue, green) can only worsen this imbalance within the body.

Unfortunately, our common habits and lifestyle cause us to suffer from a shortage of red and yellow around us. It simply cannot be otherwise, as from early childhood we usually wear white underwear and sleep in white bed linen (even though the bed linen 'fashion' has slightly changed nowadays and we can pick and choose from multicoloured bed linens, it still does not solve the problem). Nurseries, schools, offices and hospitals are usually painted white with the addition of such colours as blue, deep blue, black, green or pink.

Why are we so reluctant when it comes to red and yellow? Has it got something to do with certain superstitions and the identification of red with hell? Red is actually the colour of life (blood) and yellow represents the Sun. Maybe we should pay more attention to these colours and accept their role and importance in our life.

Red protects us from the influence of negative external factors (bad outer energy). This applies equally to people as well as to certain places and their so-called 'vibes'. Red can also ensure a deep and peaceful sleep at night. For example, wearing red pyjamas and sleeping in red bed linen can protect a child from nightmares. Red underwear can warm us up in autumn and in winter; it can increase our immunity to illnesses, calm us down and improve the condition of our health.

Yellow has a warming effect on the body and secures emotional balance. I do advise people with obesity, and especially those experiencing a constant feeling of hotness, to introduce firstly yellow colour 'therapy', followed by red colour 'therapy'. Both colours are indispensable in general wellbeing and their energy can support the body against such illnesses and diseases as asthma, allergies, colds, flu, long-lasting hypothermia, strokes and obesity or problems with the lungs, kidneys, liver, stomach, and intestines.

By absorbing the energy of these two basic colours (red and yellow) we can achieve a so-called uprooting or merging with the element of Earth. This way we are able to reach the Yin of our existence (Earthliness) and keep it in balance with our Yang (Spirituality). The energy of red leads to spiritual awakening; it changes our consciousness and opens us up to all kinds of spiritual experiences.

I personally think that a shortage of red and yellow in the lives of children and the young is one of the causes of emotional problems, aggression, mental imbalance, susceptibility to stress and negative outer influences.

| Bodily organ | Actions | Emotions | Flavours | Climates | Colours |
|---|---|---|---|---|---|
| Liver (Wood) | Straining the eyes (watching TV, reading) | Anger, frustration | Excess of sour flavour | Excess of wind | Excess of green |
| Heart (Fire) | Over-expressiveness, talkativeness and activeness | Over-joyfulness (caused by external factors) | Excess of bitter flavour | Excess of heat | Excess of red |
| Spleen (Earth) | Sitting | Worrying oneself sick, negative thinking | Excess of sweet flavour | Excess of moisture | Excess of yellow |
| Lungs (Metal) | Lying | Sadness, sorrow | Excess of spicy flavour | Excess of dryness | Excess of white |
| Kidneys (Water) | Standing | Stress, fear, anxiety | Excess of salty flavour | Excess of low temperature | Excess of blue |

Table 4. Destructive factors.

Damaging effects of external factors are characteristic of people suffering from Yang deficiency (deficiency of energy and warmth).

Introducing colours into our life requires, as anything else, common sense and moderation. Overexposure to a particular colour can be as harmful to our body as the excess of any other factor.

Even though red and yellow are the colours representing life and energy, we do not need to dress only in red or sleep in red pyjamas and red bed linen or eat breakfast in a red kitchen, on a red tablecloth or work in an office painted red. We must not become fanatical about it. Apparently, the only universal colour that does not have any negative effect is aubergine. This colour makes us feel better and helps in creative work.

## Movement – physical activity

Movement is an indispensable element of our life. There should always be equilibrium within our body between the Yin aspect of our life (relaxation, meditation and sleep) and the Yang aspect of our life (joy, activity and work). We should not damage our body with excessive work or physical activity. We need sleep in order to regenerate the substance and our body. Thanks to movement and proper breathing, we supply our body with life energy (Chi) and oxygen and improve the quality of our muscles.

A correlation exists between the quality or efficiency of bodily organs and the efficiency of our muscles. An ineffective muscle, or a group of ineffective muscles, can cause an imbalance within the whole body and vice versa – a weak bodily organ can cause tension and contractions of particular muscles. This can eventually lead to problems with body posture and consequently the dysfunction of other bodily organs. One may then experience problems with digestion and nutrition, endocrine disorders or even psychological problems. Any problem of a physical or physiological nature consequently leads to emotional imbalance.

Physical activeness and exercise involving core strength and flexibility maintain appropriate body posture and strengthen the spinal column. A strong and straight spinal column enables proper and deep breathing. An appropriate body posture and good quality of breathing enable circulation of the life energy within the central canal. And the quality of the protective outer energy, Wei-Chi, is dependent on the circulation of the energy within the central canal.

The appropriate circulation of the energy within not only the central canal but the whole body is one of the crucial conditions for good health. A free flow of energy is possible only when both the mind and the body are well balanced. In order to reach this balance we have to train ourselves to ease and relax both the mind and the body equally. This way we create the so-called Taoist emptiness, which enables the free flow of energy within the whole body. Of great help in this case are isometric exercises and relaxation.

Physical activity is always of benefit to the flow of energy within our body and to our metabolism. Even those who do not follow a healthy diet but nevertheless exercise sufficiently are of better health than those who do not practise any physical activity.

Physical activity is often advised as an element of therapy in many health conditions (diabetes, obesity, rheumatism, circulatory disease). Exercise is beneficial for those who suffer from allergies and especially from allergic rhinitis and cystic fibrosis. People who are physically inactive or who exercise sporadically should avoid condensed food such as nuts, seeds, fattening cakes with cream and food of a cooling nature.

Every living organism has a predisposition for movement and physical activity. Thus, we should not restrain it and we should be more spontaneous, joyous and active at any age.

# DEFICIENCIES AND EXCESSES OF ENERGY WITHIN THE BODY

## When do we feel cold?

The feeling of cold occurs when Yin exceeds Yang. The balance of Yin and Yang within the body is equivalent to the balance of cooling factors (Yin) and warming factors (Yang) within the body (see Fig. 13).

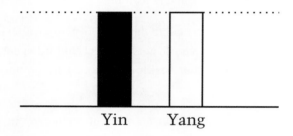

Fig. 13. Balance of energy (Yin-Yang) within the body.

The balance of energy within the body can be destroyed by:

- climate (low temperature, cold rain and wind)
- emotions of the Yin type (fear, stress, anxiety, worries)
- lack of physical activity
- bad diet.

Excessive exposure to a low environmental temperature (see Fig. 14) can slow down metabolism and blood circulation and lead to muscular contractions, shivers and a low body temperature. In this situation, the level of Yang within the body becomes insufficient to balance out the excess of Yin. If exposure to the cold environment does not last for too long, the balance of Yin and Yang can be retrieved relatively quickly. However, if the exposure lasts for too long a period, the cold penetrates into our body and destroys our bodily organs. This can be the root of many serious health problems.

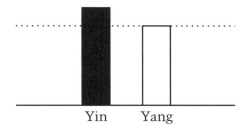

Fig. 14. Excess of Yin (impact of a cold environment).

The most typical conditions caused by cold weather (cold environment) are colds, coughs, headaches and flu. A long-lasting exposure to cold can also badly affect the heart, stomach, spleen and kidneys. In order to reduce an excess of Yin within the body, one should consume food and drinks with warming properties and dress accordingly.

Emotions of the Yin type have a destructive effect on Yang in our body (see Fig. 15). They cause a stalling of energy and lower our body temperature. The most common emotions of the Yin type are: worrying, sadness, sorrow, stress, anxiety and fear. All of these negative emotions, if experienced for a long period of time, can lead to a weakening and overcooling of the body. An effect of this process is that not only the Yang but also the Yin of our body (the nutritious fluids and essence) is slowly destroyed.

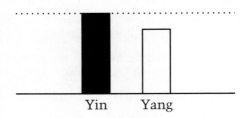

Fig. 15. Deficiency of Yang (too much emotion of the Yin type).

Emotions in general have a big impact on the functioning of the stomach and spleen, both of which are responsible for the production of the essence and nutritious fluids. If faced with negative emotions one should try to remove oneself immediately from their source. Warming food of Yang nature is very helpful in this process.

It is a matter of fact that movement and physical activity provides warmth and energy to our body. On the other hand, a lack of physical activity (see Fig. 16) slows down metabolism and blood circulation. This leads to lower physical capability, loss of muscle mass, weakening of tendons and ligaments, to stalling, blockages and oedemas, and indirectly, to obesity.

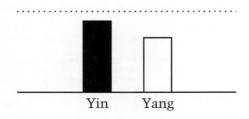

Fig. 16. Deficiency of Yin and Yang (lack of physical activity).

In this situation, a change of lifestyle is advisable. If this is not possible, then one should try to at least reduce the quantity of food of the Yin nature that is consumed and introduce to one's daily diet more food of warming properties (food with an addition of herbs and spices). In other words, one should include in one's diet more food that is rich in the energy Chi.

However, it is important to try and eventually make physical activity and exercise involving core strength and flexibility a permanent element of our life.

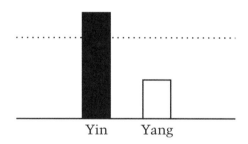

Fig. 17. Excess of Yin and deficiency of Yang
(too much food with cooling properties).

Food has a big impact on the Yin-Yang balance within the body (see Fig. 17).

Too much food of a cooling and moistening nature leads to overcooling of the body, malfunctioning of the bodily organs and accumulation of moisture and mucus. The Yang of the body is not able to deal with the spreading coldness and moisture. An effect of this process is that the level of Yang drops significantly.

This situation, when an inappropriate diet destroys the Yang of the body, is, in fact, a major cause of many diseases. Typical symptoms occurring after eating too much food of the Yin type are: a low body temperature, headaches, stomach aches, general weakness, muscular pain, diarrhoea, nervousness and apathy. In order to restore balance, one should eliminate food with cooling properties and introduce warm and freshly cooked meals.

In the situation of an excessive exposure to a cold environment (cold weather), the body can activate a defence mechanism in the form of a fever. **One should remember that fever that is a direct result of the overcooling of the body appears only in the evening or at night. If the fever appears during the day then it is a symptom of indigestion or of fire in one of the bodily organs**.

### When do we feel hot?

The feeling of heat occurs when Yang exceeds Yin.

The factors affecting the balance of Yin and Yang in this case are:

- climate (hot weather)
- emotions of the Yang type (aggression, hatred, frustration, over-joyfulness)
- too much physical activity
- bad diet.

Faced with hot weather or heat in the environment (see Fig. 18), in order to protect our body from heat damage, we usually try to adjust what we wear, eat and drink to the surrounding environment.

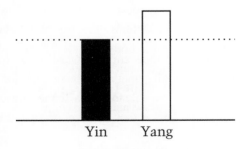

Fig. 18. Excess of Yang (impact of a hot environment).

When it is too hot in the surrounding environment, one should cool the body with cold compresses or cooling drinks, such as brewed peppermint tea or bitter chicory coffee.

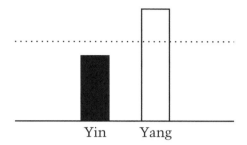

Fig. 19. Excess of Yang and deficiency of Yin
(too much emotion of the Yang type).

Emotions of the Yang type cause an 'explosion' of energy within the body (see Fig. 19). This leads to the state of Fire, which burns our internal fluids (Yin). However, if we feel that these kinds of emotions are being experienced too rarely, then we can restore the balance by eating more sweet food or doing some physical exercise (e.g. walking). Aggression and fury, but also suppressed strong agitation, can all be symptoms of a problem with the stomach, spleen or liver. If this situation occurs on a regular basis, then one should work on strengthening one's internal bodily organs.

A lack of relaxation and sleep has a destructive effect on Yin of the body (see Fig. 20) and causes many health problems. Regeneration and restoration of the substance of both the blood and the body can only happen during relaxation and sleep. Everyone should rethink their lifestyle and reflect on the notion of balance between the Yin aspect of life (sleep, rest, relaxation) and the Yang aspect of life (work, physical exercise and activity).

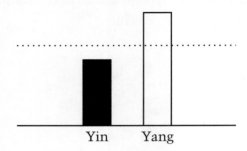

Fig. 20. Excess of Yang and deficiency of Yin (too much physical activity).

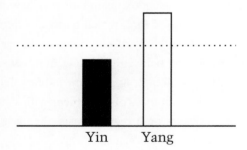

Fig. 21. Deficiency of Yin caused by deficiency of Yang – the false excess of Yang (long-lasting diet of a cooling nature).

An excess of Yang within the body (see Fig. 21) is not caused by eating too much food of strongly warming properties. It is caused rather by a deficiency of Yin (blood and internal fluids), which is always the result of eating too much food with cooling and moistening properties. This kind of food destroys the stomach, spleen and kidneys, and consequently leads to deficiency of Yin and creation of a false excess of Yang (Fire). In order to eliminate the state of the false heat we should try to strengthen the stomach, spleen and kidneys by elimination of food with cooling properties.

# TONGUE

A regular observation of our tongue's appearance can provide us with useful information on the state of Yin-Yang balance within our body (see Fig. 22). The appearance of our tongue is a reflection of our health.

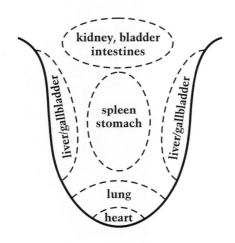

Fig. 22. Tongue areas as they
correspond to internal organs.

- A red tongue body indicates heat, Fire and deficiency of Yin.

- A dry tongue body indicates deficiency of bodily fluids and Yin.

- A pale tongue body indicates deficiency of Yang and blood.

- A blue tongue body indicates coldness and stalling of blood.

- A swollen and thick tongue body indicates coldness and moisture.

- A flaccid tongue body indicates lack of Chi and Yin.

- A pale tongue body with white coating indicates coldness, moisture and stalling.

- A red tongue body with yellow coating indicates moisture and heat (Fire).
- A cracked tongue body indicates deficiency of Yin and Yang and a weak spleen.
- A very deep ventral crack indicates a weak spleen.
- Red spots may indicate deficiency of Yin and heat.

These are only a few examples of diagnosis based on the tongue's appearance. However, the knowledge in this area is much broader.

# DISEASES

*What's right isn't always popular, and what's popular isn't always right. (Sharon M. Draper)*

To shape our own being and transform the dullness of our existence into a marvellous art of living, we need to remain humble, but humble in the sense that we do not neglect our own talents and uniqueness. We need humility which is synonymous with the simplicity of living and staying attuned to the Earth and its richness. We do not need purity and asceticism, which in fact can reduce our vitality. Instead, we need a simple and active life full of passions and various experiences.

In order to achieve this we need to free ourselves from imposed dogmas and stereotypes. Let's not be scared of freedom, decision-making and creating our own reality. Allow the voice of our Inner Self to speak to us. It is about time for us to become responsible for our own wellbeing, emotions, appearance, physical condition, health and the quality of relationships with our family and friends.

Modern medicine may be able to prolong our lives, but it does not enrich our life. It does not prevent diseases. It is more a medicine of suffering rather than a medicine of health. All of the institutions and organizations which declare themselves as protecting and saving lives instead only contribute to a multiplication of suffering and disease. And the reasons for this are simple.

The effort of the medical sector and many charitable foundations and organizations is mainly focused on helping those people who are already ill or suffering: babies, children and the young. This, as a matter of fact, unconsciously stimulates the mechanism of 'production' of the ill and suffering. These are two huge energies which stimulate one another and, as a result, create a vicious cycle. Quantum physicists would have a lot to say on this subject.

On the other hand, we do not initiate many campaigns that promote health (which could generate a similar energy). We do not give up enough money and time to embed awareness among future parents (mothers in particular) on the principles of good nutrition and bringing up children.

We do not stress enough the responsibilities of future mothers. We also do not focus enough energy on introducing appropriate standards to nurseries, kindergartens and schools, where children should be protected, looked after with care and surrounded by a friendly atmosphere.

Why do we prevent ourselves from acknowledging this very important truth that in order to grow up and shape their personalities, children need the constant assistance of adults? As a matter of fact, only an adult is able to give a child the energy indispensable to the process of formation of their body and mind. Constant interaction with their peers can badly affect the physical and emotional growth of a child. A child needs the touch and caress of an adult.

Why do we allow this initial suffering of a child to then, all of a sudden, spend all our energy on saving their life?

Why do we neglect the most basic responsibilities towards our children, simultaneously complaining about their bad behaviour and aggression?

I get the impression that the whole sector of modern medicine suffers from a lack of red and yellow. Maybe these two colours would actually make it more flexible, tolerant and non-conformist? Maybe only then would the modern medicine sector be able to gather the knowledge that would allow the protection of human life in all its aspects – physical, emotional and spiritual?

Maybe this would also help to induce the medical sector to some more self-criticism? Because it is not the biggest achievement to cure illnesses in the age of great technological progress; it is not the biggest achievement, having all these precise mechanical and electronic systems, to discover new viruses and errors in DNA. The biggest achievement would be finding out the reasons for the viruses' activity, as well as the reasons for the deformation/mutation of the genetic code. The biggest achievement would be to eliminate the causes of imbalance within the body, and the causes of many diseases, atypical personality disorders and suffering. One should stop claiming after all these years that the only causes of disease are viruses and bacteria, a deficiency of certain vitamins or mineral salts, eating too much fattening food or not enough fruit and vegetables. This is just one of the big misconceptions of our times.

How can we change the perception of the world? How to find the true cause of health problems and how to eliminate them?

With all respect for modern science and technology one should turn more towards Nature, its wisdom and rules. One should discover and accept the true nature of all the factors affecting the state of our emotional and physical balance.

By acknowledging the nature of flavours, climates, colours and emotions, we could consciously decide on our wellbeing and health. We could benefit from positive factors and avoid negative ones.

**It is rather dangerous to attempt to fight an illness without knowing its true cause. Every dysfunction within the body is a signal of a Yin-Yang imbalance, which may be caused, for example, by the wrong kind of diet or bad emotions. The elimination of an ailment (e.g. cough, runny nose, fever, stomach ache, heartburn, itch, rash, headache or backache) will only augment the imbalance, and sooner or later it will recur in another place and in a different form.**

Here is an example of the sequence of particular ailments, which in effect lead to more serious health problems. Firstly, there occur frequent colds, coughs and tonsillitis, followed by pneumonia, hernia and a heart attack, which finally results in jaundice. This example shows how important it is to stop the course of an illness at its initial stage. We can do this by eliminating causes for the overcooling of the body.

According to my observations, the major cause of the Yin-Yang imbalance in our climatic zone is food of overcooling properties. Emotions, colours and climates are secondary causes; however, experienced over a long period of time they can be very damaging too. The elimination of the causes of all sorts of health problems is especially important for children. If we overlook their conditions in early childhood, then it is more than likely that they will suffer from much more serious health problems later on in their adult life.

We must remember that a fever in children can be caused, firstly, by overcooling of the body (if high body temperature occurs in the evening or at night), and secondly, by indigestion (if high body temperature occurs in the afternoon). In the first case, one should try to warm the child up, and in the second case it is best to give the child a laxative. In both cases one should avoid giving a child food with cooling properties, such as sour, raw and cold food as well as sweets.

Spinal diseases can signify a weak and cold liver, spleen and kidneys. In such a case, one should strengthen the body by eating more food with neutral warming properties.

Gynaecological problems (early menopause, dislocation of internal organs, infertility) are usually caused by excessive overcooling of the body, a weak spleen and poor blood circulation.

Nausea, vomiting and stomach contractions, on the other hand, can be symptoms of a cold spleen, stomach and liver caused by eating too much sweet stuff, fruit and fresh salad and drinking too many cold drinks.

Chronic headaches signal an overcooling of the body and poor blood circulation. Very helpful in this case is to drink boiled coffee with added cinnamon and wrap up warm in bed for some time.

Spring fatigue is usually a result of eating the wrong kind of food during the summer and autumn and Christmas gluttony (too many sweets, citrus fruits and too much meat).

Maintaining a warm stomach and spleen and avoiding sour, raw and cold food is also good for cancer prevention.

Heartburn is a symptom of a cold spleen and an excess of heat in the stomach. One should then stay away from cheeses, sweets and cold, raw and sour food.

## Obesity

According to science, one of the major causes of obesity is a slow metabolism. A common opinion states that it is mostly caused by eating food with a high calorific count. However, this knowledge is of little comfort to those suffering from obesity. The questions: why is my metabolism so slow? or, why are calories so important in this case? – remain unanswered. The notion of metabolism is rather superficial and imprecise. Not many people are aware that obesity can be caused by a malfunctioning of certain bodily organs. They see it more as a genetic problem instead.

According to traditional medicine, the process by which, in supplying the body with appropriate nutrients, such as carbohydrates, proteins, fat, vitamins, mineral salts (in other words – matter), we obtain energy and substances necessary for the process of cell renewal, is termed metabolism.

But truthfully speaking, metabolism is much more than this. It consists of many complex processes (closely interrelated with one another) that can only happen in very specific circumstances. They are still unexplainable and unknowable by us. The process of metabolism does not depend entirely on the quantity of particular nutrients (which I mentioned above) provided by food. The most important thing in this process is the condition of our bodily organs – the stomach and the spleen in particular (the element of Earth – Centre). On their energy and efficiency is dependent the strength and wellbeing of our body and, consequently, the process of assimilation of nutrients. In order for the stomach and spleen to function properly, they need to be supplied with nutrients of the appropriate quality, that is – of the right energy, temperature and Yin or Yang nature.

Why is food energy so important? It's because it is indispensable in the process of production of the substance and life energy within the body. The matter is also very important (vitamins, proteins, etc.). But it is the energy obtained from food that stimulates certain reactions. Thus, 'dead' food with no energy cannot sustain life. We can eat healthy food, rich in vitamins and calories, but if it does not provide the necessary energy, then we can easily destroy our body. Non-energetic food gives the impression of a permanent internal emptiness and unsatisfied craving. This kind of food creates the so-called energetic emptiness. That is the reason we reach for a snack – a dessert, a cake, ice cream, an apple or sweets. But even this will not eliminate the impression of emptiness. It is in fact a long-lasting and rather unpleasant feeling.

Obesity makes one feel guilty most of the time. It causes great psychological discomfort. A healthy person will only eat when hungry or when their level of energy is low. Obese people feel the need for food most of the time because they are 'hungry for energy'.

Only fresh food retains most of its energy, e.g. fresh and ripe fruit (before storage). But whereas there is a plentiful supply of fresh fruit and vegetables in a hot climate, in our climatic zone we can only have them seasonally. That is why we have to put more effort into the preparation of food of an appropriate quality and energy.

The cooking process transforms matter into energy. In other words, the energy of fire stimulates the energy of food.

In order to eliminate the feeling of emptiness and constant hunger, we only need a few daily meals of a slightly warming nature. They should be well balanced with the Five Flavours and contain a sufficient level of energy.

Another very important factor in the process of metabolism is the nature of food, i.e. whether the food is of a cooling (Yin) or a warming (Yang) nature. In our climatic zone, we should always eat hot or slightly warming food (even in the summer). The cooling kind of food can only lead to an imbalance of the acid-base homeostasis, certain dysfunctions of bodily organs, circulatory disorders, and most of all, problems with digestion, absorption of nutrients and excretion. The organs that are most dependent on the nature of the food eaten are the stomach and spleen. The wrong kind of food can affect the functioning of both these organs. And so the process of mutual weakening begins. A malfunctioning stomach does not digest the food properly and does not supply the spleen with all the necessary energy, which makes the spleen go cold. A cold spleen, on the other hand, stops producing the right quality and quantity of fluids. In consequence, some of the bodily organs (lungs, heart, kidneys, liver) become strengthened, but in the wrong way, which is of no benefit to them. And the spleen, instead of producing nutritious fluids, starts producing moisture and mucus.

From the above, we can draw the conclusion that we should take care of what we eat and make sure that the food we choose is not only rich in vitamins but also of an appropriate Yin-Yang nature (cooling or warming food) and of a sufficient level of energy.

Food of a cooling nature (Yin) includes fresh fruit and vegetables, fruit juices, ice cream, cooling drinks, as well as pickled vegetables, cheese, fruit yogurt, milk, sweets, cakes, sugar, pasta, white rice, pork and chicken.

For an overweight person, eating large quantities of fresh salads, fruit and fruit yogurts, rice and chicken and drinking cold water can weaken the stomach and spleen (both organs become cold). No fruit-veg-dairy diet will help with weight loss but will rather cause other serious health problems. One should in fact abandon this kind of diet in favour of a more reasonable and well-balanced one. The stomach requires warm food, of a mild flavour and slightly warming nature. Only then will it be able to function properly! Sour, raw or cold food mixed together with cold drinks merely paralyses the stomach for many hours and consequently causes digestive problems! I want to remind you here that cold drinks, such as cola and other fizzy sugary drinks, beer, fruit juice and milk, not only weaken the stomach but lead to acidification of the whole body.

However, we should not entirely eliminate cooling food from our diet. In fact, with the addition of appropriate spices, and supplementary to the warming kind of food, it can be of benefit to our health. But it is necessary to take into consideration the actual season of the year and its implication for the type of diet, as well as our own health condition. For example, all fruit should only be eaten in season. Pasta should not be combined with sour sauces but with spicy meat-veg ones. Natural yogurts (not fruit ones) can be mixed together with buckwheat and fried potatoes. Spiced chicken and pork should be eaten together with cooked or stewed vegetables. On the other hand, sour soups, such as cabbage or tomato soup, should be based on a beef or calf-bone stock with the addition of a large quantity of onion, garlic, black pepper and ginger. Sweet cakes should be eaten in the late morning or just before afternoon and not mixed with fresh fruit or fruit juices. Instead we should drink some boiled natural coffee.

Modern medicine does not acknowledge the impact of cold food on metabolism, when it is in fact a crucial factor and is the key to the fight against obesity.

Mood swings, lack of mental balance and concentration, excessive excitability and nervousness – these are all very characteristic emotional states which often affect overweight and obese people. They are all the effects of a malfunctioning spleen and stomach. Every time there is an imbalance in the spleen or stomach, we automatically crave something sweet.

But sweets are merely a temporary treatment for nervousness and frustration. For example, eating a cake may give us a short-lasting feeling of comfort and relaxation. Each emotion consumes our energy, leading to weakness and exhaustion. Our body then requires the sweet flavour, which strengthens the spleen (Centre) and balances out our emotions. Craving sweet or sour food also occurs when a particular bodily organ is in a state of fire. This type of craving often accompanies obesity. Thus a piece of cake or a biscuit will not help but will only increase the problem.

I would also like to remind you that the sweet flavour should not be identified only with sugar.

Overweight or obese people often try to explain their weight problem as being the result of genetic or hereditary predispositions. However, by acknowledging the problem and changing one's dietary habits and lifestyle, one can effectively reduce or even eliminate obesity. Genetic or hereditary predispositions are merely the effects of long-lasting exposure to destructive factors, such as a wrong diet and lifestyle, long-lasting stress, difficult circumstances (e.g. wars) and the illnesses of our ancestors or environmental and climatic determinants.

Obese people, more than anybody else, need physical activity. It not only enables the body to obtain an increased level of oxygen but also accelerates the process of metabolism of carbohydrates, fats and proteins. Metabolism of carbohydrates is the fastest and metabolism of proteins the slowest. A by-product of metabolism is glucose. Glucose is our basic fuel. Through oxidization (burning) of glucose we obtain the energy required in various processes within the body.

In order to initiate any form of metabolism within our body we need a permanent supply of the so-called life energy. A low level of energy can cause problems with absorption of nutrients. To run the process of oxidization of glucose effectively within the body one needs an appropriate quantity of blood rich in oxygen, which the spleen, lungs and heart are responsible for supplying. Of great benefit in this case is physical activity and proper breathing. A shortage of oxygen leads to ineffective oxidization and, consequently, excesses of glucose, which then, together with insulin, are stored in the liver, muscles and body fat. This type of disorder, if it lasts for a long period of time, leads to pancreatic exhaustion (diabetic problems), fatty liver or even cirrhosis. And these are problems that typically concern obese people!

The only way to escape obesity and cleanse the body of the excess of mucus (toxins) is through warming of the body and stimulation of the internal organs.

One can only achieve this through the implementation of a warming type of diet. Proper food will help the body to regain its optimal weight, and the body will be able to self-regulate the quantity of food it takes in.

Implementing a diet that is well balanced with the Five Flavours and run accordingly to the rules of Yin-Yang can guarantee an effective loss of weight!

## Problems with cholesterol

An excessively high cholesterol level can be a symptom of an overcooling of the body and/or bad metabolism. One of the symptoms of having a long-lasting high cholesterol level is atherosclerosis.

The substance responsible for maintaining the appropriate level of cholesterol within the body is lecithin. In the presence of an enzyme containing vitamin B6, lecithin undergoes the process of synthesis. However, this particular enzyme is only activated in the presence of magnesium. Consequently, one cause of problems with cholesterol can be either a lack of vitamin B or a low level of magnesium. Assimilation of magnesium, on the other hand, depends on the quality of the processes within the endocrine and digestive systems. The process of assimilation of magnesium can be restricted by an excess of calcium in food.

Food rich in cholesterol, such as butter and eggs, is not directly responsible for a high cholesterol level. In fact, a drastic reduction of these two products in our daily diet can lead to a significant deficiency of vitamins A and D (leading to osteoporosis) and choline – a substance responsible for the proper functioning of the liver (leading to Alzheimer's). A very low cholesterol level is also very bad for our health. It leads, amongst other things, to emotional problems and depression.

Problems with high cholesterol levels mostly affect those who suffer from a low body temperature, exhaustion and an excess of moisture (mucus) within the body. They are mostly obese people, diabetics, people with a high blood pressure and circulatory disorders. Bad diet, an excess of emotions and stress can all lead to problems with cholesterol levels.

The cholesterol level can be lowered by implementing in our daily diet cooked or stewed vegetables (avoid raw vegetables). Cooked fibre is easier to assimilate in the body and thus it is much more effective. Our diet should be of a warming nature and provide a sufficient quantity of fibre, vitamins A, B and D, as well as magnesium. There are not enough of these elements in raw fruit, fruit juices, fresh salads and cheeses. But fatty fish, olive oil, garlic, onion and oats, for example, are foods that are extremely rich in these elements and therefore highly recommended.

## Osteoporosis

Osteoporosis is one of the diseases of affluence, and in recent years it has become a real problem within society.

Osteoporosis is very common in developed countries, where the consumption of milk and dairy products is high. A susceptibility to osteoporosis also depends on sunlight; thus the disease occurs more commonly in countries of the cold climatic zone where the amount of sunlight is limited.

Milk and dairy products are consumed by nearly one-third of the world population. The other two-thirds of the world population do not include dairy products in their daily diet. And it is within the latter group that the rate of osteoporosis is very low. It has also been discovered that women who live in cities are more likely to get osteoporosis than women living in rural areas. This is because women living in rural areas spend more time outdoors and are physically more active.

Can we prevent osteoporosis? Of course! But firstly we need to know the causes of this particular condition.

Osteoporosis is a disease associated not only with a general weakening of the body (of the spleen and lungs in particular), but also with a deficiency of Yin caused by a long-term deficiency of Yang (Chi and warmth).

Osteoporosis is a disease caused by a deficiency of calcium in the bones. One of the causes of this deficiency is a low level of calcium in the blood and over-activity of the parathyroid glands. Both of these symptoms are interlinked with many other processes. Very characteristic of osteoporosis are also deficiencies of magnesium, zinc and vitamins A and D, as well as a low level of oestrogens and testosterone. Many of those affected by osteoporosis may also suffer from liver and stomach dysfunctions, premature menopause and other gynaecological disorders; the state of their skin, nails and hair is also affected badly. All of these symptoms are typical of a state of overcooling of the body.

The loss of calcium in the bones is not necessarily caused by a deficiency of calcium in our daily diet. In fact, it can be otherwise. Too frequent consumption of food rich in calcium (low-fat cheeses, yogurts, hard cheeses), without the simultaneous assimilation of the appropriate quantity of vitamins A, D and E, as well as magnesium, can block calcium assimilation and lead to a dysfunction of cell metabolism in bones. Thus, an excess of calcium in food can weaken internal organs and lead to many health disorders.

We can also assume that osteoporosis begins when the state of overcooling of the body becomes permanent.

What causes the overcooling of the body? Well, first of all, it is our own ignorance and lack of knowledge of the nature of food and its impact on the body. Using the example of osteoporosis, one can notice that the nature of food really matters. We may think that we eat healthily. We eat low-fat cheeses, skimmed milk, fruit yogurts, hard cheeses, fruit, fruit juices and fresh salads, without even thinking that all of these products are of a highly cooling and moistening nature and that they lead to excessive production of moisture and mucus and, simultaneously, to a deregulation of the acid-base homeostasis. This affects the assimilation of vitamins (A, D, E) and mineral salts (magnesium, zinc, iron, selenium). Thus, 'overdosing' on calcium can damage particular organs. It can also be one of the causes of allergies, skin rashes, coughs, catarrh and nervousness. Many of those who suffer from osteoporosis drink large quantities of milk and eat lots of dairy products in the hope that it will make them feel better. But it does not. It actually makes things much worse for them.

## How to prevent osteoporosis?

Most of all, we should avoid the overcooling and acidifying types of food and food rich in calcium. We should eat more warming food, based on cooked vegetables with the addition of spices, meat, grains, peas and beans. At the same time, we should avoid cold drinks, ice cream, sweets, fresh salads and fruit. Overall, we should provide the right level of vitamins A, D and E, as well as magnesium.

## Allergies

I am very familiar with this particular problem, as I fought my personal duel with allergies for over six years. They were causing me very unpleasant symptoms, lasting for months, such as a runny nose, itchiness of the skin when exposed to sunlight, and also an itchiness and over-sensitivity of the eyes to light.

Thanks to acknowledging the true nature of certain food products and implementing a suitable diet for my own needs, all of the above symptoms were gone within three months of beginning my 'special' treatment. So, for instance, I have now been able to sunbathe for the past seven years. I also do not need to wear sunglasses and I no longer have a problem with a runny nose. Years of experience and observation made me believe that the true causes of my allergies were not pollens or sunlight or allergen products, but the wrong kind of food which conflicted with the needs of my own body.

The influence of environmental contamination is a totally separate problem in this case. A strong and healthy body will be able to resist environmental influences. On the other hand, a weak and malnourished body will be more susceptible to all sorts of health problems.

Certain allergic symptoms, such as skin rash, runny nose, itchiness, are simply alerts to a Yin-Yang imbalance within the body. We should learn to decode these signals and react to them in the right way. They are a source of information about the state of our internal balance.

Antihistamines and all sorts of anti-allergy drugs eliminate the symptoms but cover up the real causes of allergies, which consequently develop into much more serious health problems such as: asthma, jaundice, kidney disorders, diabetes, high blood pressure, ulcers, obesity and heart disease. Not all of these symptoms will occur at the same time. However, I do know a person who did suffer initially from allergies, then underwent symptomatic treatment and eventually ended up with all of the above health problems (as well as the allergies).

If our health depends so much on the Yin-Yang balance, then our food should be well balanced too (there should be a balance between the cooling and warming types of food). If we eat too much of the cooling types of food (milk, cheeses, sour soups, fresh salads, pasta, rice, pork, fruit juices, water, ice cream and sweets), our body cools down and becomes weak and susceptible to all sorts of health problems, including allergies.

If someone suffers from allergies they should carefully watch their own dietary habits. They should avoid the above-mentioned overcooling food products. They should also always remember that getting rid of the nagging symptoms is not equivalent to proper treatment. I shall repeat once more – they should seek and eliminate the true causes of their problems, which are very often caused by the wrong diet and a bad lifestyle.

Medical doctors prophesize that in the near future one in every two people will suffer from allergies. And I must admit that I share their opinion. However, it is not only the fault of the environment we live in but also our unwise lifestyle and nonsensical dietary habits.

In fact, the causes of allergies are rather prosaic. And, as it turns out, we can prevent or even cure most cases of allergy. The only condition is to stop following the healthy eating mythology.

The biggest victims of allergies are children. Never-ending problems with a runny nose, colds, asthma, tonsillitis and coughs prevent them from living a normal and happy life. And it is all down to an overcooling and weakening of their body. Treated symptomatically they eventually end up with anaemia, kidney and liver dysfunctions, or intestinal disorders, as well as many other health problems.

The health of our children depends on us adults. We are responsible for what they eat. Very often we feed them with too much fruit, fruit juices, fruit yogurts, cheeses, cold drinks, ice cream and sweets, without thinking about the consequences. Let's change these dietary habits, so our children can have a happier and healthier life.

## Peptic ulcer disease and gastric hyperacidity

Peptic ulcer disease and gastric hyperacidity are usually caused by an imbalance within the element of Earth (stomach, spleen and pancreas) and a weak (cold) liver. The imbalance is the result of an improper diet and intense negative emotions. Both of these factors are closely interlinked.

The wrong kind of diet can be responsible for such conditions as emotional hyperactivity, mental imbalance and increased susceptibility to stress. But it can also happen the other way round – long-term exposure to stress can cause emotional blockages within the solar plexus and, consequently, lead to a dysfunction of the stomach, spleen, pancreas and liver.

A weakened liver deregulates the flow of energy within the meridians of the stomach, spleen and pancreas. The symptoms of this weakened state are nausea, vomiting, strong and painful stomach contractions, flatulence, chest pain and headaches. All these symptoms are a sign of a significant weakening of the body. They are very often accompanied by shivers, the feeling of coldness (low body temperature) and strong catarrh.

A bad diet, and especially too much consumption of the acidifying and cooling types of food and/or emotional blockages, can have an adverse effect upon the spleen and pancreas. In this situation, the body does not receive a sufficient quantity of internal bodily fluids and essence. As a result, the stomach suffers an imbalance (lack of Yin). This manifests itself as a false excess/fire (heartburn, a burning sensation within the stomach and oesophagus, flatulence, anxiety, a constant craving for food or nausea and vomiting). In this situation, even a small but unsuitable snack or drink, such as milk, fruit yogurt, sweets or raw fruit, can cause an almost immediate sensation of burning in the stomach. There are various medicines for gastric hyperacidity. They neutralize the excess of acid fluids in the stomach and protect its lining. However, they do not cure the condition but merely calm its symptoms.

In order to get rid of gastric problems, one should eliminate from one's diet the foods responsible for causing this kind of condition. One must, most of all, strengthen and warm up the stomach, spleen and pancreas.

For over twenty years, I myself suffered from peptic ulcers, gastric hyperacidity and heartburn. During that time, I followed the dietary recommendations given by doctors. I ate mostly white cheeses, hard cheeses, raw fruit and vegetables, white meats and lettuce and I drank milk, fruit juices, linseed brew, cabbage and potato juice. I avoided fats, meat, spices, onion, garlic, broths and stocks based on bones. Unfortunately, the condition only intensified and I suffered from horrible pains almost every day.

Once I became familiar with the Yin-Yang theory and its dietary rules, and especially after I learnt about the nature of the food I was eating, I understood the true cause of my problems. I discovered that food which has a cooling and weakening effect on the spleen and causes an imbalance within the element of Earth, also has highly acidifying properties. Thus, all those laboratory statements on the acidifying and alkaline properties of certain foods are totally irrelevant. The biggest influence on the acid-base homeostasis is the properly functioning element of Earth (spleen, pancreas and stomach), which is possible only when we maintain the Yin-Yang balance in our daily diet.

It is a misconception that gastric hyperacidity and heartburn are diseases of excess. The true cause of these conditions is overcooling and weakening within the body, and especially within the element of Earth (spleen, stomach). Only by warming our body within we can restore the balance.

Recently, popular new kinds of treatment for gastric problems have appeared. These are based on medicine of highly warming properties, which contains ginger, cayenne pepper and other spices. In this case, a propolis tincture based on ethyl alcohol may also be very helpful.

This is my advice to all suffering from gastric problems: stop eating food with cooling properties! Give up milk and cheeses, raw fruit and vegetables, fruit juices, cold drinks, beer and cold water; cut down on sweets and cakes, rice and pasta, and try replacing sugar with honey. I can guarantee that within a short period of time all your ailments will vanish. I have tested this treatment on myself and I have not suffered from any gastric problems for the last seven years.

**Diabetes**

Diabetes is a result of an imbalance within the element of Earth, i.e. weakened spleen, pancreas and stomach. It eventually affects the lungs, kidneys, liver and blood circulation. Diabetes is associated with a deficiency of Yin and a false excess (heat) in the stomach. The deficiency of Yin is caused by overcooling of the body and a deficiency of Yang. The major reason for weakening of the spleen and pancreas is a bad diet. Diabetes is often associated with genetic and hereditary predispositions. However, these predispositions do not necessarily need to be activated. Being aware of one's predisposition to diabetes, one should immediately modify one's family's dietary habits. Diabetes is mostly caused by the cooling type of food and food low in energy, such as sugar, sweets, cheeses, milk, fatty pork, fresh salads, fruit, fruit juices, cold drinks and ice cream.

The term 'diabetes' refers to a family of illnesses caused by a cold spleen, pancreas and stomach. The large scale of this disease should make us aware of the fact that our dietary habits need to improve. There is a prognosis that 50% of society will suffer from diabetes in the near future. **A question arises: why are we more and more ill, even though we follow our doctors' advice?**

The core of each diabetic's diet should become cooked meals with large quantities of vegetables, onion and garlic, and with additional spices, such as cinnamon, ginger, nigella and turmeric. They should also eat different kinds of meat, all of them low-fat and home-cooked. However, they should avoid ham and sausages. Small quantities of fatty fish, olive oil and butter are also advisable. They should also give up at all cost white bread, yeasty cakes, creamy cakes, sweet desserts, fruit yogurts, cold drinks and water.

**Coeliac disease**

Coeliac disease is a disorder of the digestive system. It is often associated with babies and children; however, adults can also be affected by this condition. It is one of those diseases which leave an indelible mark on our health.

A baby's susceptibility to coeliac disease depends on its mother's diet (especially during pregnancy). Also, switching too early from breastfeeding to solid food or formula can lead to acidification of a baby's under-developed bodily organs. The most undesirable products in babies' diets are cow's milk, wheat flour and sugar. Instead, these should be replaced with goat's milk, millet flour, corn flour or oat flour and honey. Children fed with the latter types of food grow and develop much better.

How can we prevent coeliac disease? First of all, mothers-to-be should exclude from their diet food of a cooling nature and that which is low in energy (Yang). Even though all medical recommendations say otherwise, future mothers-to-be should actually avoid eating large quantities of fruit, fresh salads and dairy, and refrain from drinking fruit juices and cold water. Otherwise the woman's body will suffer from the overcooling effect and become too weak to provide the foetus with all the necessary substances and energy. This results in babies being born weak and susceptible to diseases. The diet during pregnancy should be rich in warm and cooked food based on various vegetables, onion, garlic, grains and spices.

Coeliac disease does not mean only intestinal problems and a strong reaction to gluten. It is also associated with an overcooling of the body and a dysfunction of the stomach, spleen, pancreas and liver. Thus, when dealing with coeliac disease in children, one should avoid gluten as well as all types of cooling food, e.g. fruit, fruit juices, fresh salads, cheeses, cow's milk, sweets, ice cream, chicken, pork, ham and sausages. The diet should, in this case, consist of cooked food of a mild flavour (mostly cooked vegetables and grains). Soups for younger children should be based on beef, veal and turkey stock, and for older children on lean goose and all kinds of liver. Children should also be introduced at an early age to onion, garlic, herbs and spices.

## Cystic fibrosis

The core of this disease lies in an over-production of mucus within the body and its eventual accumulation in the lungs, sinuses and other bodily organs. Mucus causes problems in breathing and the functioning of internal organs. One of the main causes of cystic fibrosis is a malfunctioning spleen (cold spleen), which, instead of producing internal fluids, produces mucus. The malfunctioning of the spleen can only be exacerbated by food of a cooling nature, such as milk, cheeses, sugar, sweets, ice cream, fruit, fruit juices, cold pork (ham and sausages) and chicken.

All of these products should be eliminated from one's diet. Especially when the disease affects children, one should make sure that their daily diet consists mostly of warm food or food of warming properties. An overcooled and weakened body will always produce mucus.

The diet of future mothers-to-be and small babies is very important as a means of prevention of this disease (the same applies in the case of coeliac disease). If it is really necessary to replace breastfeeding with a substitute diet then one should at least make sure that it does not include cow's milk, wheat flour, sugar and processed baby food. All of these products are in fact strongly acidifying and actively stimulate the production of mucus.

## Our problems with children

We all agree that the health and wellbeing of our children is a priority to us adults. But very often, in the quest for the best possible conditions for our children's growth and development, we put too much trust in the public health sector and other institutions. And I personally think that there is a large dose of hypocrisy in this attitude.

We also know that in order to stay healthy, our offspring need to be properly and regularly fed. But feeding them with yogurts, fruit and fruit juices is of doubtful benefit to them. Let's be honest about the food we often give to our children. What do they actually eat? The whole candy industry (sweets, bars, chocolates), dairy industry (yogurts, cheeses, ice cream), soft-drinks industry (cola and other fizzy sugary drinks) and fast-food chains make fortunes on the 'small' consumer. Our children are potential clients to all of these businesses. Why? Because we allow them to be. The time our children spend outdoors without our supervision is most likely the time they will try to get hold of the chocolate bars, fruit juices, fast food, yogurt, cakes or fizzy drinks. It is because of our own convenience or lack of sufficient knowledge on healthy dieting or lack of time and enthusiasm that we do not fight all of these bad habits. Eventually, we silently accept our children's dietary misbehaviour.

Unfortunately, aggressive advertising, as well as the stereotypes and fashions circulating among the young, is a negative influence on our children and usually too difficult for them to resist.

Do we adults have anything to say in self-defence? I do not think so. To understand the scale of the problem, it is enough to go into schools and randomly ask how many children bring their own homemade lunch to school, how many of them eat homemade dinner or supper, how their parents organize their daily meals, or how many of them are actually being told by their parents about the dangers of eating fast food.

We are responsible for the awareness of our children.

How can we say that we care about our children when we consciously let them eat dairy products that come from mass production and are very often contaminated with dangerous substances? For those who are still unaware, the milk used for production of most of the dairy products comes from cows which are fed with fodder including ruminant meat and bone. Isn't it against common sense and nature? Cows are herbivores and should not eat any animal material. How can it possibly not affect the quality of milk and dairy products?

It is dishonest of adults to make money out of children's lack of awareness and vulnerability in the first place, to then spend some of this money on wonderful medical equipment and children's health centres. Who has got the biggest interest in all of this? We should realize that our children's health problems were probably caused by our own ignorance, negligence, convenience or simply turning a blind eye to the problem.

Thus, we should remember once more:

• An excess of fruit, fruit juices, fresh salads, sweets, ice cream, yogurts, cheeses and cold drinks leads to allergies and asthma.

• An excess of milk, cheeses, fruit, fruit juices, sweets and ice cream can cause anaemia in children.

• An excess of milk, cheeses, yogurts, sweets, fruit and fruit juices makes our children more susceptible to colds.

If you really care about your children's health then firstly confess your mistakes and then start introducing changes to their dietary habits before taking them to the doctor or a hospital.

## Old age and its ailments

*We do not get sick because we grow older, but we grow older because we get sick.* (Author unknown)

With all my determination and responsibility, I claim that ailments associated with old age derive directly from unreasonable dietary habits during the early stages of our life. Many doctors admit that they are not familiar enough with geriatrics and are not able to explain why some illnesses progress with age.

We all know that the level of life energy we receive at birth will gradually decrease with age. We should try and protect this energy by supplementation with energy obtained from food and the environment. Therefore, older people's diet should be rich in energy and all the necessary nutrients. This means that in order to stay healthy, older people should eat absolutely all foodstuffs but with the addition of adequate spices and composed in such a way that they are easy to digest and assimilate. They should, however, reduce the portions of their meals but rather eat more often.

In order to maintain proper cell metabolism and blood circulation one should use products rich in vitamin B, and also vitamins A, D and E, magnesium, zinc, iron and calcium. Unfortunately, pills and tablets are ineffective in this case. Also, fruit and fruit juices contain only trace quantities of these nutrients. We should also remember that in order to digest fruit and vegetables properly one needs a strong and healthy digestive system and a high level of the energy Yang. Thus, in order to protect their internal organs, old people should avoid eating raw foods. The same food products, only cooked (boiled, fried or roasted), remain as nutritious as they are when raw but are much easier to digest and assimilate.

All these popular modern dietary recommendations for the old merely prove a lack of knowledge on the actual processes happening within the body of an older person, as well as an unwillingness to understand the real causes of such health problems as Alzheimer's disease, paralysis, heart attacks, diabetes, degenerative arthritis and rheumatism.

Very dangerous for older people is a diet based on white and low-fat cheeses, skimmed milk, low-fat yogurts, lean meat, white bread and raw fruit, steamed or raw vegetables, with no added spices.

How can one prevent osteoporosis whilst at the same time avoiding sunlight, eggs, butter, full fat milk, fatty fish and meat?

How can one prevent Alzheimer's disease whilst eating large quantities of fruit, fresh salads, yogurts, chicken, vitamin C and drinking fruit juices? I mean, this kind of diet is very hard on the liver and kidneys.

How can one prevent degenerative arthritis, rheumatism or rheumatoid arthritis whilst avoiding soups, broths, spices, beef, lamb, onion and garlic?

How can one cure high blood pressure and atherosclerosis whilst eating sour and cold food, such as yogurts and fruit, and drinking large quantities of water?

How can one recommend that someone with heart problems lose weight and eat large quantities of fruit and fresh salads and drink water? It is against a common sense and simply not achievable.

I am convinced that a reasonable approach towards problems with old age will help to avoid unnecessary suffering.

Dear Reader,

If you read my books with acceptance and decide to discipline yourself – you have a lot to gain! Always. You will start observing changes within your body.

You can gain a lot by helping sick children and adults who suffer from allergies, asthma and atopic eczemas. You can help for sure.

Conventional medicine is helpless in this case. Steroids and antibiotics bring temporary relief, but in reality they only augment these problems and do not cure them at all, whereas dietary discipline is a guarantee of a speedy recovery.

Similar rules apply to colds.

In order to prevent recurring problems with sore throats, ear pain, diarrhoea and catarrh, one simply needs to understand the true nature of colds.

My advice on dietary discipline has helped in many difficult cases, such as problems with getting pregnant, gastrointestinal bleeding, rheumatic pain, chronic headaches, shingles, and so on.

Many years of experience, consultations, talking on the phone and participating in internet forums have assured me of the positive effects of dietary discipline.

There are many examples of the effectiveness of this method. For example:

- It helps to fight obesity;
- It regulates all kinds of digestive problems, such as flatulence, constipation, diarrhoea, heartburn, reflux;

- It stabilizes cardiovascular problems;

- It also stabilizes, or in most cases even eliminates, lung diseases;

- This method can also help with parasitic diseases.

Another positive change observed with this method is stabilization of emotional problems; it increases the level of our energetic capacity and thus reduces our susceptibility to depression.

If only you want to do it and are conscious enough of what might happen, then start cooking and observe the changes within and around you.

# Examples of the effectiveness of the therapies proposed in this book

### A 50-year-old woman

The woman was completely cured from allergies (itchy and watery eyes, hay fever and skin irritation from sunlight). She stopped suffering from peptic ulcer pains, flatulence and indigestion. Her eyesight improved, her body weight stabilized (she lost about 5kg of weight). The condition of her skin, nails and hair improved a lot. Her physical fitness became even better than when she was 30 years old.

### A 50-year-old man

He lost 20kg of weight and his body weight stabilized. He stopped having problems with tonsillitis, coughs and emotional ups and downs.

### A 26-year-old man

The man suffered no more stomach aches, flatulence, indigestion, tonsillitis, a runny nose and coughs. His physical fitness improved significantly.

### A 27-year-old woman

She stopped having problems with eczema, hair loss, tonsillitis, coughs and a runny nose. Her eyesight improved, too.

### A 50-year-old woman

The woman stopped suffering from liver and stomach dysfunctions, headaches, back aches, nausea, vomiting and general tiredness. Her physical and mental condition improved significantly.

### A 13-year-old boy

The boy stopped suffering from skin rashes, a runny nose and coughs.

## A 19-year-old woman

She brought up her baby according to the rules from this book, and from birth onwards the baby never had any health problems.

## An 82-year-old man

After eliminating sour, cold and raw food from his diet, the man suffered no more stomach dysfunctions, shingles and allergies.

## A 30-year-old woman

The woman stopped suffering from rheumatic pains and arthritis, both of which had troubled her since early childhood. Her general physical and mental condition improved significantly. She also lost about 10kg of weight and her whole body weight stabilized.

## A 22-year-old breastfeeding mother

After eliminating fruit yogurts, rice and milk from her diet, and reducing the quantity of fruit and sweets eaten, her baby became much calmer and suffered no more contractions and stomach aches.

## A 25-year-old breastfeeding mother

After eliminating all cold and raw food from her diet, as well as cold drinks, her baby stopped suffering from strong stomach aches and diarrhoea.

## A 56-year-old man

After recovering from jaundice and gallstones, the man decided to go off all raw, sour and cold food and sweets. From then on, he had no more liver or gall bladder problems.

## A 56-year-old woman

After recovering from cancer, the woman went off all sour, raw and cold food, and from then on had no more intestinal problems.

### A 14-year-old boy

After reducing the quantities of sweets, fruit, raw salads and cold drinks in his diet, the boy stopped suffering from chronic colds, tonsillitis and coughs.

### A 73-year-old woman

She had had problems with her liver all her life. They all stopped after she decided to go off fresh salads and abandoned her evening habit of eating apples. She also rarely had traditional coffee, as it always made her feel bad afterwards. After she started drinking boiled coffee instead, her general wellbeing improved.

### A 52-year-old woman

She was a daughter of the woman mentioned above and she suffered from problems similar to her mother's. They stopped bothering her when she eliminated all raw and sour food from her diet.

### An 85-year-old man

Throughout his life, the man did not eat any fresh salads and fruit. Also, his only source of fat was butter. After detailed medical tests he was claimed to have the liver of a young person.

### A 26-year-old mother

Her breastfed baby was nervous, was vomiting and was not putting on weight. When the mother went off fruit, fresh salads and yogurts, and reduced the quantities of cheeses and sweets in her diet, the baby became healthy and grew and developed properly.

### A 60-year-old woman

After eliminating sweets, fruit, fresh salads and cold drinks from her diet, the woman stopped suffering from kidney disorders, leg pains, headaches and frequent colds.

## A 27-year-old man

Throughout his childhood the man had suffered from obesity. He eventually became obsessed with his weight and ate only very small portions of food. Once he decided to go off sweets, fresh salads, fruit and cold drinks, he could finally eat proper meals and still did not put on weight.

## A 54-year-old woman

She suffered from chronic liver problems, flatulence and skin irritation from sunlight. All of these ailments stopped after she resigned from eating sweets, fresh salads and fruit and drinking cold drinks. Her condition and physical fitness improved significantly at the same time.

# NUTRITION AND HEALTH

The term 'balanced nutrition' should not be confused with such notions as a 'healthy product', 'healthy food' or an 'unhealthy product'. The only things that are unhealthy are all kinds of excess and a one-track diet. The core of healthy and balanced nutrition is a varied diet comprised of many products of differing nature that complement and strengthen each other. Many doctors and dieticians claim that the value of particular food products depends on their nutritious compounds, such as proteins, calcium, vitamins or cholesterol. However, this kind of approach is improper, dishonest and harmful. Avoiding some products and overindulging in another type of product can eventually lead to various health problems. This kind of attitude (which, according to the rules of balanced nutrition, would be seen as a major dietary mistake) is never taken into account by modern medicine in the process of diagnosis. Instead, the diagnosis is based on the analysis of the compositional value of a diet. Looking into these modern dietary recommendations, one can find that they are often contradictory and misleading, and can in fact lead to serious health problems.

Certain nutritious compounds, such as proteins, carbohydrates, fats, mineral salts and vitamins, do not occur in nature as separate elements and cannot be added to our diet as separate products. All of them, however, can be found in plant and animal matter, which we consume in the form of various food products.

In the process of food preparation, an important role is played by all sorts of additional food products and spices, as they accelerate the digestion and assimilation of nutrients. Also important in this is the process of cooking (boiling, stewing, pickling, etc.), which releases the energy from food and makes it easier to assimilate within our body.

All nutrients are generically and energetically interdependent. Therefore, our body needs to be in a good psycho-physical shape in order to be able to deal with the digestion and assimilation of nutrients and the absorption of energy and essence. These processes can be compared to very complex chemical reactions. Thus, in order for these processes to run properly and achieve the desired final effect, one has to take care of the quality and proportion of the components included, and ensure the required technical parameters, such as time, temperature, pressure, etc. If any aspect of this chemical reaction (such as the processes of digestion and assimilation of nutrients) is incorrect, then the whole process becomes distorted.

Important factors, amongst others, are: the quality of the components, the order of their addition to one another, the presence of an appropriate catalyst, and the duration of the process.

The process of digestion and assimilation of nutrients can run with no obstacles only when we eat well-balanced meals, which are prepared according to the Five Flavours order, with the addition of spices (catalysts), and at a temperature suitable for our stomach (warmth). We certainly should avoid drinking cold drinks with warm food. Preparation of food is a great skill and one should avoid randomness! Inventiveness and creativeness in the kitchen are advisable, but only when accompanied by the rule of the Five Flavours order.

A monotonous type of diet (e.g. eating mostly sour or cold food) can be very harmful to our body and lead to the weakening of particular bodily organs (e.g. spleen, stomach or liver). Badly balanced food secures only minimal absorption of nutrients, as weakened bodily organs are unable to deal with the process.

Unfortunately, we have lost our primary intuition with food. We no longer know what is good or what is bad for us. That is why we need to learn this skill again. This book is a first step towards good health. We should not follow fashions for certain types of products, such as fruit juices, yogurts or cheeses, and be paranoid over vitamins. We should firstly learn about the nature of certain products and use them wisely. I would advise you to think twice before eating something. Ask yourself if you need to eat a particular product in order to keep the balance within your body and if it will make you feel better.

Our health problems, and their related deficiencies of vitamins and minerals, are always the result of bad digestion and assimilation of nutrients, not the other way round. We have to consider then what is causes this. Are we perhaps eating too much cold food of cooling properties that is too low in energy? Or is it caused by an excess of certain emotions (which are, by the way, always affected by what we eat)?

Symptomatic diagnosis of illnesses, as well as the qualitative and quantitative approach towards nutrition, only strengthens our so-called 'linear approach' towards the human body. This kind of approach is typical of modern medicine, which does not take into consideration the true rules of Nature. But the fact is that the human body, just like the whole of Nature and the Cosmos, is a structure of interdependent, harmonized and unified elements and systems which cannot exist by itself.

The scientific perception of the human body leads to the creation and accumulation of new problems that are impossible to examine and solve. This approach also makes us treat Nature and its rules as our worst enemies (irritating sunlight and pollens, severe winters, dangerous viruses and bacteria). But we must remember that complex medical equipment (which I do appreciate) will never replace all the warmth, loving and caring which we can give to each other and which can be the true solution to our ailments.

I would like to remind you here that our wellbeing and the process of proper absorption of nutrients depends on the condition of our stomach, spleen and other bodily organs, as well as on the preparation and composition of our diet.

**Vitamins and mineral salts**

By presenting a few chosen vitamins and mineral salts, and the complexity of interdependences between them, I would like to make you aware of the unconditional necessity of treating your body as one whole, and the food you eat as a source of energy and balance. The following information will help you to understand how important it is to maintain a varied diet and, on the other hand, how damaging a monotonous and one-track diet can be.

## Vitamin A

Vitamin A can be found in such food products as butter, eggs, fish-liver oil and liver. It has multiple functions. For example, vitamin A is responsible for the state of our skin, mucous membranes and good vision. It also plays an important role in the process of cellular growth and development and in the maintenance of the reproductive system. The appropriate level of vitamin A and magnesium supports the functioning of the thymus, a gland responsible for the immune system.

Vitamin A is normally stored in the liver and can be released only in the presence of zinc. Thus, application of vitamin A without a simultaneous application of zinc is ineffective and will not balance out the deficiency of vitamin A within the body. However, one should also remember that assimilation of zinc can be disturbed by an excess of calcium within the body.

Vitamin A can be obtained from carotene. Carotene, in turn, is usually found in yellow and orange fruit and vegetables, as well as in the green parts of a plant. In the presence of enzymes, carotene transforms inside the intestinal tissue and in the liver into vitamin A. The creation of vitamin A can also be supported by the thyroid hormones; however, a large quantity of vitamin A weakens the functioning of the thyroid. The appropriate level of vitamin A can be difficult to sustain when, among others, problems occur with thyroid dysfunction, weak intestines, liver disorder, bad digestion and a deficiency of zinc. Eating too much raw fruit and vegetables can also decrease the level of vitamin A. A deficiency of vitamin A is one of the initial factors leading to osteoporosis.

Cooking vegetables does not destroy carotene; it enables its easier assimilation within the body. Both vitamin A and carotene should not be exposed to light, as they are very sensitive to it.

## Vitamin D

Vitamin D enables easier absorption of calcium and phosphorus. It also secures the appropriate proportion between both elements and their most beneficial concentration level in the blood and bones. Thus, a lack of vitamin D is one of the major causes of osteoporosis.

The body can synthesize vitamin D when sun exposure is adequate. However, certain illnesses can affect this process. These are: peptic ulcer disease and hyperacidity, pancreatic and intestinal inflammation, liver and kidney disorders, parathyroid gland dysfunction and a deficiency of magnesium.

Vitamin D can be found in such food products as butter, eggs, fish, fish-liver oil and liver.

I know that all these products contain large quantities of cholesterol and are not recommended by dieticians. But one should understand that the level of cholesterol in our body mainly depends on the quality of our metabolism. Also, when it comes to exposure to sunlight, opinions may vary. I personally think that a reasonable approach to sunbathing can be beneficial to our health.

Products rich in calcium, such as hard cheeses, yogurts, skimmed milk and white cheeses, and products of a strongly cooling nature (fruit, fresh salads, fruit juices, ice cream and sweets) can inhibit the absorption of vitamin D. Eating too much of these products can eventually cause serious health problems.

## Vitamin E

Vitamin E is one of the strongest antioxidants. A deficiency of vitamin E can cause muscular contractions (same as a deficiency of magnesium). Vitamin E can be found in pearl barley, oats, eggs, butter, vegetable oil, peas, beans, nuts, broccoli, parsley and other greens. Vitamin E is particularly good for all sorts of heart problems. However, an excess of vitamin E can be rather harmful to the heart.

## B vitamins

B1 – thiamine, B2 – riboflavin, B3 (PP) – niacin, B6 – pyridoxine, B7 (H) – biotin, choline, inositol, PABA, pantothenic acid, folic acid.

B vitamins are components of enzymes; they stimulate enzymes from within. They are responsible for the wellbeing of our nervous system, cellular metabolism and all other processes within the body.

B vitamins dissolve easily in water. They can be found mostly in meat, giblets, buckwheat and pearl barley, oats, whole-wheat bread, nuts, seeds, almonds, eggs and such vegetables as cauliflower, cabbage, broccoli, Brussels sprouts, onion, garlic, potatoes, spinach, beans, peas and mushrooms. Fruit, on the other hand, contains trace quantities of these vitamins.

A diet which is mostly based on lean beef, low-fat white cheese, lettuce, fruit juices, fruit and yogurts can lead to a deficiency of B vitamins. Cooking does not destroy B vitamins. But in order to retain most of them during the cooking process, it is best to stew the food in a small quantity of water (which is kept afterwards) or in its natural juice. Eating too much carbohydrate (sweets, cakes, pasta, white bread, etc.) can increase the need for B vitamins.

## Vitamin C

I think that the role of vitamin C in the popular so-called 'healthy' diet is much overrated. I also think that a varied and well-balanced diet provides a sufficient level of vitamin C. Vitamin C is one of the antioxidants (but not the most important one) that can be easily found in ordinary food products such as ginger, cabbage, broccoli, carrots, onion, garlic, etc. Sour fruit and vegetables are a great source of vitamin C, too, but we need them only to balance our diet with the sour flavour and strengthen the function of the liver. We must remember, though, that an excess of vitamin C, and especially in the form of tablets or large quantities of fruit and fruit juices, can destroy the liver and kidneys and become the root of many health problems. That is why one should never 'overdose' on vitamin C.

Cooked vegetables, such as potatoes, cabbage, broccoli, Brussels sprouts, cauliflower, peppers, provide enough of the required level of vitamin C.

## Magnesium

Magnesium is one of the most important elements that take part in the process of metabolism and maintain the proper functioning of the immune system. This particular element takes part in the synthesis of proteins as well as in the process of cell division. It reduces the toxic effects of the element lead and enables its faster excretion from the body. It also calms and soothes the nervous system and muscles. Nervous impulses depend on the transfer of calcium and magnesium ions. A deficiency of magnesium can inhibit this process and cause nervous excitability. It is interesting that all the symptoms of tetany, muscle twitch or over-excitability usually recede after receiving a magnesium injection (and not, despite common thought, a calcium injection). For the harmonious processes of the nervous system, the ratio of calcium to magnesium should be 2:1. Analogically, the bigger the deficiency of magnesium, the larger the susceptibility to stress.

Calcium inhibits the absorption of magnesium. Thus, eating large quantities of dairy (milk, cheeses, yogurts, etc.) can lead to a deficiency of magnesium within the body. The process of magnesium absorption is usually supported by the thyroid, parathyroid and pituitary glands. It is quite obvious, then, that magnesium levels within the body depend on the condition of these glands.

Drinking beer significantly lowers magnesium levels within the body. This can eventually lead to heart attacks and arteriosclerosis. Other symptoms of a low magnesium level are painful contractions of the cardiac muscle and contractions of leg muscles.

Grains, peas, beans, nuts, almonds, poppy seeds, cocoa, whole-wheat bread and also green plants are rich sources of magnesium. Fruit contains only trace quantities of this element. Cheeses, on the other hand, contain too much calcium to make the absorption of magnesium possible.

Magnesium is important for the proper functioning of the thymus, the central organ of our immune system, and the liver. Magnesium salts prevent the formation of larger kidney stones. Indirectly, magnesium also regulates cholesterol levels (lecithin can synthesize only in the presence of an enzyme containing vitamin B6, and this particular enzyme is only activated in the presence of magnesium). Low magnesium levels lead to a deficiency of vitamin D, which in turn is responsible for bone mineral density. Thus, osteoporosis is always a symptom of a deficiency of magnesium within the body! One should also remember that too much stress and a nervous lifestyle can not only reduce our life energy (Chi), but also lower the level of magnesium in the body. Magnesium, selenium and cobalt together can prevent DNA errors. We must remember that it is not some supernatural powers that damage our genetic code but, in fact, very specific physical factors.

## Calcium

Calcium is the main constituent of bones and teeth, and alongside phosphorus, zinc and magnesium, it is also an important constituent of muscles, blood and bodily fluids. Calcium cannot be absorbed on its own. It can only happen in the presence of magnesium, zinc and vitamins A and D.

The parathyroid hormone plays a key role in calcium metabolism. When the calcium level in the blood gets too low, the parathyroid hormone automatically activates the process of rinsing calcium out of the bones. In the case of hyperparathyroidism (which is usually an effect of an overcooling of the body), the level of calcium in the blood is constantly increased due to a continuous process of rinsing the calcium out of the bones.

This inevitably leads to osteoporosis. The excess of calcium also inhibits the absorption of magnesium, zinc and iron. A high calcium level in the blood, so typical of hyperparathyroidism, can cause calcification of vessels and bodily organs and results in kidney stones and gout.

Animal and vegetable food products are great sources of calcium. Animal products that are rich in calcium include: fish, eggs, meat, stock based on bones and fatty dairy (rich in vitamin D, which enables absorption of calcium). Vegetable products rich in calcium are: whole-wheat flour, peas, beans, greens, garlic, broccoli, kohlrabi, cabbage, Brussels sprouts, chickpeas, lentils and many more.

## Zinc

Zinc is required for the process of releasing vitamin A from the liver and in the process of carbohydrate and protein metabolism. In other words, zinc is very important for balanced growth and development. It also helps in iron absorption.

Meat, especially chicken and turkey, and liver are great sources of zinc. Other food products rich in zinc are: mushrooms, eggs, nuts, beans, peas, whole grains, onion, garlic and fish. On the other hand, fruit, fruit juices, milk and other dairy products are very low in zinc. Also, drinking large quantities of black tea can lower the levels of zinc in the body; black tea is rich in oxalates, which inhibit the absorption of zinc.

## Iron

There is only 3–5g of iron in the whole body mass, yet in terms of its importance to our health, the role of iron cannot be overestimated. But despite the fact that iron cannot be excreted from the body, most people (children, teenagers and women in particular) suffer iron deficiency.

Iron deficiency can lead to unstable mental development in babies and children, but also to anaemia (a rather common disease nowadays), and can also badly affect the immune system. Too much calcium, sugar and sweets in our diet also inhibits the production of antibodies. And, as we already know, a properly functioning immune system is also dependent on magnesium, zinc and vitamin A.

Iron deficiencies within the body are mostly caused by a bad diet. For example, milk and dairy, so popular with children, teenagers and older people, contain almost no iron at all. Besides, they contain calcium, which inhibits absorption of iron from food.

The sour flavour is very important in the process of iron absorption. Very useful in this process are both vitamin C and hydrochloric acid. Thus, any wheat products, vegetables or meats should always be balanced out with the sour flavour. Eggs should also be accompanied by this particular flavour. Iron absorption depends also on the presence of zinc and magnesium within the body.

Fruit and fruit juices contain trace quantities of iron, magnesium and zinc. Exceptions are plums (plum jam), dried dates and raisins. On the other hand, vegetables, wheat products, legumes, eggs, fish, meat and poultry are rich sources of iron.

## Selenium

We only need trace quantities of selenium. Together with magnesium, zinc and iron, selenium is responsible for the condition of our immune system and our resistance to all sorts of illnesses, from a common infection to cancer. Selenium is also good in the prevention of genetic errors.

A diet based mostly on sugar and carbohydrates leads to selenium deficiency (its absorption becomes impossible).

Selenium can be found in large quantities in sea salt, eggs, whole grains, corn, but, best of all, in garlic and mushrooms.

* * *

I have only briefly outlined the properties of some of the most important, in my opinion, vitamins and mineral salts. One should always remember that all of them, both vitamins and mineral salts, are very important to our health and will only be effective when combined together with other elements.

In order to secure all the necessary elements of our body of, we should compose our diet in a conscious and rational way. All meals should be well balanced with all Five Flavours and suitable for the particular season of the year.

What we should always remember!

- The condition of our immune system depends on the supply of magnesium, zinc, iron and selenium to our body.

- A deficiency of magnesium, zinc and B vitamins increases our cholesterol levels.

- An excess of calcium and a diet based mostly on fruit, fruit juices and sweets inhibits the absorption of magnesium, iron and zinc within the body.

- Zinc is indispensable for the process of releasing vitamin A from the liver.

- The assimilation of nutrients, renewal of cells and calcium absorption can only happen in the presence of vitamin A.

- Vitamins D and A prevent osteoporosis and ensure proper cellular metabolism.

- **The most important vitamins and minerals can be found not so much in fruit but in meat, giblets, grains, beans and vegetables (especially in leeks, garlic, onion and cabbage).**

- **The process of cooking (with covered lid) does not destroy vitamins, but makes them easier to absorb.**

# FOOD PRODUCTS

## Dairy

Cow's milk is not really suitable for humans. Only calves are able to absorb all the goodness and nutrients contained in cow's milk. Human breast milk is the only milk that can offer a similar benefit to people.

Below I present some data on cow's and human breast milk and the compositional differences between them. Cow's milk is not suitable for humans because it contains many more mineral salts (Ca/Calcium, P/Phosphorus) and proteins than the human body can deal with. These large quantities of minerals are beneficial to the growth of a calf but not a child. Besides, cow's milk contains casein (a type of protein) which is very difficult to digest for children, producing a kind of spongy matter in the stomach.

| | Proteins [g%] | Fat [g%] | Carbohy-drates [g%] | Calcium [mg%] | Phospho-rus [mg%] | pH |
|---|---|---|---|---|---|---|
| Human breast milk | 1.2 | 4.0 | 7.0 | 33 | 15 | 7.2 |
| Cow's milk | 3.3 | 3–3.5 | 4.8 | 125 | 95 | 6.6 |

Table 5. Composition of human breast milk and cow's milk.

Human breast milk contains substances suitable for the delicate and still not entirely developed alimentary canal of a child. It contains antibodies, light proteins and the appropriate quantity of carbohydrates and fats. It also contains two times more selenium and six times more vitamin E than cow's milk.

|  | Human breast milk | Cow's milk |
|---|---|---|
| Proteins | More albumins (albumin milk) | More casein (casein milk) |
| Fat | More unsaturated fatty acids (linoleic acid, oleic acid) | More saturated fatty acids |
| Vitamins | More fat-soluble vitamins | More water-soluble vitamins |
| Other elements | Lipase, diastase | |

Table 6. Nutritional value of human breast milk and cow's milk.

**Children need milk until the age of 3, and the best is their mother's milk. During this period, the baby's body produces lactase, an enzyme indispensable for the digestion of lactose (sugar), and rennin, an enzyme needed for the digestion of proteins.** After this period, we should introduce food products that are rich in calcium to our child's diet. For example, vegetables, grains and meat can provide even more and better-balanced nutrients than cow's milk. We need only make sure that there is enough vitamin D (sunlight, butter, eggs) and that our child's digestive system is warm enough to function properly.

Cow's milk contains large quantities of calcium and casein, which inhibit the functioning of the stomach, spleen and intestines. It also intensifies the production of mucus and acidifies the body. Americans claim that, next to beer, cow's milk is the most acidifying food product. And I do agree with their viewpoint entirely!

Due to its acidifying properties, cow's milk should be avoided especially when suffering from peptic ulcer disease, hyperacidity, rheumatism, arthritis, kidney disorder, a cold liver, headaches, high blood pressure, constipation, intestinal disorders, psoriasis and allergies. Cow's milk should not be given to children who suffer from allergies, tiredness, hyperactivity, cystic fibrosis, coeliac disease, and who are susceptible to tonsillitis, flu, coughs, stomach aches and headaches.

If someone decides to drink milk then they should always add some garlic to it. This way the absorption of calcium becomes possible. Despite appearances, skimmed milk is of no value; it lacks vitamins A, D and E and many bio-elements.

A similar argument applies to low-fat, white cheese. White cheese is of a cooling nature and sour flavour. Thus, eating too much white cheese can trigger an extensive production of mucus. This type of cheese should always be served with the addition of cream or butter and spices, which enable easier absorption of calcium. White cheese is not good for older people, as it can weaken the functioning of their liver, kidneys, heart, lungs and stomach.

Cow's milk is not a medicine against osteoporosis! Osteoporosis is an effect of hormonal imbalance within the body and problems with calcium absorption. The latter can be improved by introducing a diet rich in vitamins D and A (eggs, butter, cod-liver oil, plus sunlight) and food of a warming nature. It is impossible to increase calcium absorption by eating more products rich in calcium; in fact, it achieves the opposite. A varied daily diet provides a sufficient quantity of calcium. One should only make sure that there is enough vitamin D in it and that our stomach, intestines and glands function properly. As I mentioned earlier in the book, two-thirds of the population of the world do not drink milk and thus do not suffer from osteoporosis.

Sour milk is of a cooling nature. Thus, in our climatic zone, cow's milk should be served fresh (or at most one day old) and should always be accompanied by food of warming properties, such as buckwheat or fried potatoes with cumin and onion, and drunk only during hot summer days. In general, fresh or sour milk should not be mixed with sour fruit and sugar. This combination only increases the cooling properties of milk and leads to an extensive production of mucus. Fruit and sugar are both of a cooling and moist nature. Thus, all milkshakes and milk cocktails based on milk and fruit, as well as fruit yogurts, are not advisable in our climatic zone, and have nothing to do with a healthy diet! They merely cool and acidify our body, slow down our cellular metabolism and weaken the stomach, spleen and intestines.

Yogurts are typical in the diets of, for example, Bulgaria. In its climatic zone, however, yogurt is an indispensable element of the diet. Bulgarian cuisine is of a strongly warming nature and needs yogurt to balance out the excess of Yang (fire). Bulgarians do this by adding some yogurt to their meals, which consist mostly of lamb with the addition of large quantities of spices, garlic and onion. The Bulgarian climate is rather hot and its summers are long and sunny. Thus, the cooling properties of yogurt bring a balance to the daily Bulgarian diet. This principle also applies to other Mediterranean countries, where people eat or drink fresh yogurts but with no added fruit.

In contrast, in our climatic zone, and especially in diets mixed with fruit and sugar, yogurts are a very bad idea! Central European cuisine is known for using lots of pork, sauerkraut, cucumbers and modest quantities of spices. Also very popular are compotes, jams, cakes, sweets, fruit juices, fresh salads and fruit. All these products have a cooling effect on our body and yogurt can only intensify such a state.

Yogurt is very good and important part of a diet in hot climates. In our climate we should eat it only when suffering from an inflammation of the large intestine or from liver and heart fire. Yogurts are healthy, but not for everyone! People who suffer from tiredness, a low body temperature, indigestion, allergies, catarrh, coughs or headaches should only eat yogurt occasionally!

One should remember that there are no universal products that are good for everyone! Eating yogurt only because there is this common opinion that 'yogurts are healthy' can, in the long run, bring more harm than benefit!

If there is a need to use dairy in the cooking process then it is best to use goat's or sheep's milk and cheeses. Goat's and sheep's milk has a warming nature and contains more albumins than cow's milk. It is also not so heavy on the stomach and does not contribute as much as cow's milk to the production of mucus. In fact, goat's and sheep's cheeses eaten in moderation can be very good for our health.

Hard cheeses, according to research by Prof. A. Szczygiel from Poland, contain highly condensed quantities of calcium and proteins. Thus, one or two slices of cheese can provide the daily allowance of calcium to the body. And for this reason, we should not be tempted to reach for more dairy products afterwards (yogurts, milk, ice cream, cottage cheese, etc.).

One should also remember that there is a lot of calcium in other food products, too. A varied diet with lots of added spices, but also a well-functioning digestive system capable of coping with calcium absorption, and a reasonable exposure to sunlight, are the answers to maintaining the appropriate calcium levels. Too much cheese, on the other hand, means too much protein and calcium. An excess of calcium within the body can lead to the failure of certain bodily organs.

Hard cheeses should not be mixed with cold drinks, sour fruit or fresh salads. Thus, if we want to add some cheese to pizzas or pasta, we should always accompany it with some hot spices, onion and garlic.

France is the motherland of cheese. French people eat large quantities and different varieties of cheeses. And there is a specific reason for this particular dietary habit. Namely, French housewives have always had a very economical approach to life. In the old days, meat used to be very expensive and hard to come by. Cheeses were, however, obtainable the whole year round. Thus, in order to fill the gap in the substantial type of food, French women would often serve their families cheese instead of meat.

But nowadays we have to ask ourselves if cheese boards, so popular to serve as an after-dinner treat, are indispensable from the nutritionist's point of view? Or are they merely snobbery?

## Meat

Meat has great nutritious value. It contains proteins that are easily absorbed, important macro- and micro-elements and many vitamins (mostly B vitamins). Thanks to its specific nature, and cooked in the right way, meat can be a great source of energy and nutrients. It also has some healing properties.

Meat is an indispensable element of our daily diet, especially in our climatic zone. In fact, people of the mild and cold climatic zones have never been herbivorous. Meat used to give them strength and a chance of survival in the harsh weather conditions.

Nowadays, we have a problem with recognizing the nature of different kinds of meat (which of them are of a warming and which of a cooling nature). We also do not know which spices go with what type of meat. Another problem is that we eat far too much meat in relative proportion to other food products.

Thus, first of all, we should learn more about meat and then use it for our own benefit.

When it comes to the preparation of meals containing meat, we still very much follow the methods and recipes of our grandmothers. However, there is a difference between now and then. In the old days, our cuisine used to be much simpler, based on seasonal food products typical of our climatic zone. And most meals used to be cooked and served warm. Sweets were a rare luxury and fruit was only eaten in season. There were no fruit juices, compotes and cold drinks. Hard cheeses were also difficult to come by and we used to eat only small quantities of white cheese.

Nowadays, people still tend to eat traditional food – schnitzels, steaks, roast pork and beef. But at the same time, many of us try out fashionable new recipes and different cuisines, advertised broadly by the media. However, they are often not suitable in our climate.

We do also travel much more nowadays. We get to know different countries, their culinary traditions; we admire the effects these cuisines have on people's health. It seems that we are largely fascinated by Mediterranean and Asian types of cuisine. We try to copy them by eating, for example, large quantities of citruses, which are actually of no real nutritional value in our climate. The interesting fact is that, even in these hot countries, people usually eat at least two cooked and warm meals a day. And this fact seems to escape our attention. They also eat lamb and beef with lots of cooked or stewed vegetables, including onion and garlic. Fruit, on the other hand, is eaten in rather small quantities, mostly to refresh and protect from the heat.

We should not have a selective approach towards these foreign cuisines and their traditions. These culinary cultures have been created for generations to serve the people according to their nutritional needs. That is why we should not pick and choose elements from other culinary traditions and apply them in our cuisine. The climate we live in requires following certain rules concerned with our four seasons and the cold weather conditions where most days of the year are cloudy and cold.

Eating meat used to be very common in our culture. It is only recently that our attitude towards meat has started to change and we have begun to question whether we should or shouldn't eat it. Many of us wonder if eating meat is really necessary and if we have the right to kill animals for food.

But vegetarianism is not actually typical of our culture, tradition and climate. Our ancestors were never vegetarians. They had to eat meat in order to survive. The only time when people reduced meat consumption was when an ascetic lifestyle became a part of religious beliefs.

Vegetarianism was brought to Europe in the 19th century from India, where it was and still is an important element of Hinduism. No other religion requires vegetarianism. But whilst it is easy to be a vegetarian in Calcutta (the climate, plenty of fresh fruit and vegetables, etc.), maybe in California, too, it is absolutely impossible in central Europe!

Mystics of Tao believe that meat cooked with lots of vegetables, and especially mushrooms, loses its 'meaty' properties and becomes a vegetable itself. According to them, any form of asceticism is bad for the spirit, because it destroys the body and weakens the life energy. Asceticism does not amplify our connection with Nature but directs all our attention and energy towards our own self (ego). Asceticism does not guarantee a higher level of spirituality. Our body is a gift from our Creator. Thus, taking care of it, filling it with the right energy and adjusting it to the rules of Nature is our obligation. By weakening our body, we only weaken our spirit. And a weak body is prone to all sorts of bad influences from the outside.

We are a part of the food chain, and it is absolutely normal that one species becomes 'food' for another species. The rules and norms of co-existence within this chain are rather simple and we should all accept them. But, at the same time, we should be thankful for what has been given to us. The Creator has given us this wonderful variety of things not in order to practise asceticism but to grow and develop properly. I am sure that there will be a time when we will finally stop eating meat, but for the moment, and in this particular phase of our development, we still need it. Thus, let's not rush the process! Do take care of your bodies wisely and try to live for other people. Leave Nature to run its course, because human interference can only mess it all up!

The question whether to eat or not to eat meat is irrelevant. We should rather watch the amounts of meat eaten and pay more attention to the ways in which we cook it, so it can give us energy and even help in some of our health problems. Generally, we eat far too much meat and often cook it with the addition of the wrong kind of spices and combine it with unsuitable food products.

Eating large quantities of meat can be very dangerous for our body, as meat stimulates the spleen to intensify its production of bodily fluids. However, by adding the appropriate spices and food products and simultaneously taking into consideration their true nature and flavours, meat can have a strengthening and nutritious effect on the body.

But when we eat large quantities of meat, and especially ham and sausages, and mix it with sour foods, such as fresh salads, sauerkraut, pickled gherkins and cold drinks, or very often with sweets, desserts and ice cream, then the spleen starts producing the so-called pathological moisture and mucus and, at the same time, stops producing the nutritious kind of fluids. This causes serious disorders within the body. An excess of mucus leads to cardiovascular diseases, obesity, diabetes, kidney disorders, and consequently to the heat diseases (fire), such as high blood pressure, paralysis and heart attacks. The body eventually becomes malnourished (weak spleen = deficiency of bodily fluids). Also, the cell metabolism and our immune system are affected badly and we become susceptible to all sorts of diseases and the detrimental influence of certain external factors.

## Types of meat

**Chicken** belongs to the element of Wood. Mass-produced chicken meat is of a cooling nature and slows down the functioning of certain bodily organs, especially the liver. Thus, eating it too often can overcool the body. Chicken is recommended when dealing with the heat diseases, such as liver fire, heart fire or lung fire.

Taking into consideration the nature of chicken, pure chicken broth is not advisable. It should also contain other types of meat, such as beef, veal or lamb. Chicken should always be cooked and eaten together with the skin, which is of a strong Yang nature. This way the cooling (Yin) nature of chicken meat is balanced with the warming (Yang) nature of the chicken skin. Chicken fat eaten in moderation does not have an impact on the level of cholesterol.

There is this opinion that chicken meat is healthier than beef or pork. This is not true. Each type of meat has its own nature and eaten in excess can have a different effect on the body.

Chicken should be cooked with the addition of various spices, e.g. ginger, chilli, black and white pepper, garlic, marjoram and turmeric. Then, it is best to stew it under cover with some onion. We should serve chicken with potatoes, chips, buckwheat, pearl barley or rice, but rice with some hot spices. On the other hand, we should avoid mixing chicken with pasta, fresh salads and sour salads made, for example, from tomatoes, sauerkraut and pickled gherkins, because all of these foods only intensify the cooling nature of the whole meal. And this can lead to certain side effects and ailments. Chicken is best served with boiled or stewed vegetables.

**Duck** also belongs to the element of Wood. It is of a cooling nature. It reduces heat. Thus, duck is best for those who suffer from haemoptysis (blood-stained sputum) and fever.

Eating too much duck can cause a stalling of energy, diarrhoea and weakening of the spleen. However, prepared in the right way and eaten in moderation, duck can be very nutritious and healthy.

**Lamb** belongs to the element of Fire. It is of a warming nature. It strengthens the spleen, stomach and intestines. It has a warming effect on the body, replenishes the energy and physical strength and strengthens bones, spinal column, knees and tendons. It is very good for those who suffer tiredness, overcooling, hernias or after post-natal exhaustion.

It is best to cook a small piece of lamb (about ½ kg) for over five hours in about 5l of water with some garden angelica and ginger. The liquid should be reduced to 3l. Store this in a fridge and drink a small cup of it three times a day. You can also make broths and soups based on lamb stock or simply stew the meat with some spices (pepper, ginger, onion, garlic) and vegetables.

Lamb is the most suitable meat in our climatic zone. It is also very tasty. Lamb broth, for example, tastes rather excellent.

**Beef** belongs to the element of Earth. It is of a warming nature. It strengthens the spleen and stomach, eliminates the effects of long-lasting overcooling and tiredness, replenishes energy, renews blood and strengthens bones and tendons.

It can be used in broths and soups. But it is also very good when boiled or stewed on its own or with some added vegetables. Broth based on beef liver stock with onion, ginger and some egg yolks is a great treatment for a weak liver, problems with eyesight, muscular atrophy, anaemia and low weight.

You can also roast beef with the addition of some spices, but the best way is to cut it into small pieces and stew together with vegetables. The choice of vegetables may vary depending on our preferences. If we want to create a beef dish which will be warming then we should add onion, leeks, garlic and black pepper. We can also stew beef in red wine. However, this dish is highly warming and we should eat it only when very cold or tired. Soups based on a calf-bone stock (best are bones with bone marrow) are very nutritious and energizing. We should boil the bones for three hours and then, shortly before the end of cooking, add some vegetables.

If we want to neutralize the excess of Yang in beef then it is best to stew it together with some button mushrooms, cabbage, tomatoes and some spices.

**Rabbit** belongs to the element of Earth. It is of a cooling and refreshing nature. It neutralizes inner heat and is best for such conditions as heart fire and liver fire.

You can make some broth out of it or simply stew with some spices. Eating too much rabbit can weaken the bodily organs (overcooling).

**Goose** belongs to the element of Earth. It is of a neutral and slightly warming nature. One should avoid goose meat when suffering from an excess of the so-called hot moisture. Otherwise, it replenishes the energy and nourishes the stomach, spleen and other bodily organs.

Goose is very good in soups and broths. However, roast goose is still the most popular dish. But, unfortunately, it is very rich in fat. We can reduce or at least balance the fat by adding some spices, e.g. ginger, black pepper and turmeric.

**Pheasant** belongs to the element of Metal. It is of a slightly warming nature. Pheasant broth with some turmeric, cumin, black pepper, onion and salt is very good for strengthening both the stomach and the spleen. However, it needs to be consumed on an empty stomach. Pheasant is most recommended for strengthening the body during autumn. It replenishes energy and improves the functioning of particular bodily organs. Soups based on pheasant stock are simply the best in this case.

**Turkey** belongs to the element of Metal. It is of a neutral warming nature. Among all the different types of meat, turkey meat is the most neutral. It also has strengthening and nourishing properties. Turkey can be eaten quite often; however, always with the addition of appropriate spices. Turkey does not weaken any of the bodily organs. Thus, we can use it freely in broths and soups (both meat and bones). The most nutritious are turkey legs because their bones contain bone marrow. We only need to break or crack the bones before cooking. We should also eat all cooked turkey cartilage because it has a strengthening effect on the liver. Turkey should be mixed together with many vegetables and spices.

**Pork** belongs to the element of Water. It is of a cooling nature. It stimulates production of moisture and mucus. It also slows down the functioning of the bodily organs.

Pig farming was introduced in Europe at the turn of the 18th century. Thus, pork has not got a long tradition in our cuisine. It is more typical of Southeast Asia, where pork is very popular and known for its cooling properties. Asian people cook pork with the addition of appropriate spices and food products, which make pork more nutritious and good for their health. Europeans adopted pork in their cuisine without sufficient knowledge of its nature and the appropriate ways of preparing it. The consequence of this is many health problems.

In order to make pork easy to digest and make sure that it will not cause any health problems, such as obesity, cirrhosis, strokes, diabetes, we should mix it and cook it together with carefully chosen spices and food products. Pork is best with spices and vegetables of a warming nature, such as cumin, ginger, paprika, white and black pepper, onion, garlic, basil, turmeric, marjoram and rosemary.

Pork can have medicinal properties for various health problems. For example, it is very good in the so-called heat illnesses, which destroy internal fluids. In such cases, pork moistens and replenishes Yin. But one should understand a bit more about this matter before using pork for medical purposes.

Pig's trotters with the addition of white wine vinegar and some spices are also very good. They improve blood and blood circulation, but also strengthen tendons and joints. For example, stock based on pig's liver can stimulate production of blood; it is very nutritious and good for the liver, eyes, tendons and joints too.

**Pork ham and sausages** belong to the element of Water. They are of a cooling nature. They should be eaten together with warming food products which stimulate digestion, e.g. mustard, raw onion, all kinds of pepper, horseradish and spicy chutneys (tomato and plum chutneys).

A ham or a sausage sandwich should always be served with a slice of pickled gherkin, onion and pepper. Plain ham or sausage sandwiches are not advisable for us. We can also make sausages more nutritious by frying them in one spoon of vegetable oil with the addition of herbs, pepper and ginger. This also tastes very good cold.

However, I would like to suggest making your own homemade meats. They can be cooked, stewed, roasted, always with added herbs and spices. We can also make our own homemade pâtés, using all kinds of meat and some liver.

Pâtés are especially liked by children and men, and with the addition of spicy sauces are even more nutritious than ham. Cooking meat for a long time boosts it with energy and makes it easier to digest.

**Pigeon** belongs to the element of Water. It is of a neutral nature. It is very good for tiredness, low body weight and high body temperature. Pigeon strengthens the liver and kidneys. Soups and broths based on pigeon meat are most nutritious.

**Sea fish** belong to the element of Water. They are of a cooling nature, and thus should be eaten in moderation and with the addition of appropriate spices.

It is advisable to eat fatty sea fish at least 1–2 times a week (e.g. mackerel, halibut, sardines and tuna). They contain specific fats and valuable vitamins that help to regulate blood pressure and cholesterol levels in blood. Fatty sea fish are also good for blood circulation. It is best to eat fresh or smoked fish but, for example, canned tuna or sardines are also very good (see: Recipes).

**Freshwater fish** also belong to the element of Water. They are of a neutral but slightly warming nature.

One of the most nutritious fish is carp. It strengthens and replenishes the energy, and is best after surgical operations and labour, when it renews the internal bodily fluids. It is also very good to eat carp during pregnancy and during the breastfeeding period. All freshwater fish are very good for kidney problems.

## Preparation and consumption of meat

There are many different ways of preparing meat. Depending on what food products and spices are added and the way in which it is cooked (boiling, frying or roasting), one can increase or decrease the warming nature of meat (make it more Yang or Yin).

In order to increase the warming nature of meat, one should add some bitter, sweet and hot herbs and spices (chilli, cayenne pepper, ginger, nutmeg, cloves, black pepper, hot paprika, cinnamon, thyme, marjoram, rosemary, sage, summer savory, tarragon, cumin, mustard plant seeds and other) together with some onion, leeks and garlic.

We can also increase the warming nature of meat by stewing it with some wine or vodka or by frying, roasting or spit grilling. However, meat of a strong Yang nature should be avoided by those who suffer from heat conditions, such as fever, inflammation, liver fire, heart fire, lung fire or left kidney dysfunction.

In order to increase the digestibility of meat we should season it appropriately. This rule applies especially to chicken and pork, both of which are very popular in our cuisine. Because of their cooling nature, they can have a weakening effect on the bodily organs. Only with the addition of carefully chosen spices can we reduce the cooling properties of these two meats.

We should pay attention to the preparation of meat and eat it in moderation. It is best to stew meat with vegetables, which add nutritional value to and increase the digestibility of our meals. Use small portions of meat, chop them into pieces and stew with large quantities of various vegetables. I recommend using your own favourite recipes; only adjust them slightly by balancing them with the Five Flavours and appropriate herbs and spices.

## A few suggestions on how to increase digestibility of meat

Before, during, and after eating meat, one should avoid cakes, sweets, ice cream, and drinking cold drinks.

On most occasions meat should be eaten with boiled or stewed vegetables. If someone has a craving for fresh salads then it is best to serve them together with grains or potatoes. We should also avoid mixing meat with raw fruit; however, boiled or stewed fruit complements meat very well. Each different type of meat should always be seasoned with the appropriate spices (especially chicken and pork).

For supper (or dinner, if it is a late meal) it is best to eat warm meat of a warming nature and avoid eating too much chicken.

Ham and sausages are of a cooling nature, thus they are best fried with some added herbs and spices. When possible, we should try to replace them with boiled, stewed or roasted homemade meats.

From time to time, it is advisable to have some lard with spices (this is especially good for young people).

Also, despite appearances, ham hock, cooked with vegetables and spices, and served with some horseradish or mustard (but without beer), is healthy and easy to digest.

## Vegetables

Most vegetables are of a cold and moist nature (Yin). Only onion, garlic and leeks are of a warming nature (Yang). Eating large quantities of raw vegetables of the Yin nature can lead to an overcooling of the body and extensive production of moisture and mucus. This can slow down the functioning of the stomach, spleen, pancreas and other bodily organs.

Alongside cereals, vegetables are the basic element of our nutrition. Thus, we should eat them all year round and make sure that we prepare them according to our needs. Boiled, stewed and roasted (or fried) vegetables with the addition of warming herbs and spices are very good for us. The biggest advantage of this is that they are easy to digest and absorb into the body. During the cooking process we only lose trace amounts of the vitamins contained in vegetables. In fact, by cooking them for a very short time and under a cover we secure most of their nutritional value.

By using a variety of vegetables we can be sure that our body receives all the necessary vitamins, mineral salts and fibre. And by adding some onion, garlic and leeks we can increase the warming nature of every single meal. Let's incorporate into our daily diet the consumption of such vegetables as carrots, parsnips, parsley roots, celeriac, beetroot, cabbage, broccoli, kohlrabi, cauliflower, turnip, peas, beans, lentils, broad beans, and, very importantly, greens. We should always try to add to our meals some celery leaves, parsley, chives, dill, the leaves of leeks, garlic leaves or kohlrabi leaves. Vegetables are a source of B vitamins and vitamins E and C, carotene and all the required mineral salts.

Fresh salads are good for us, but only in the summer when there are plenty of fresh vegetables around. They have a refreshing effect on our body and make our diet more exciting. However, the way we prepare and mix fresh salads with other food products is quite important. First of all, we should eat fresh salads only when our body is capable of digesting the raw vegetable properly. Lunch hours are best for eating fresh salads. However, do not mix them with meat but with grains, potatoes, soups or stewed vegetables instead. Meat, on the other hand, is best eaten in the evening for dinner or supper. We should always remember that fresh salads are of a cooling nature; thus, in autumn and winter they should be replaced with stewed or boiled vegetables. The longer we store vegetables, the less energy they contain. However, through the cooking process we replenish them with the missing energy.

Fresh salads are difficult to digest. Thus, those who suffer from a deficiency of Yang (a weakened stomach, pancreas, spleen, intestines, malfunctioning liver or kidneys) should reduce them in their diet.

It is a misconception that fresh salads are good for obese people. Yes, they fill them up and do not provide many calories. But in the final analysis, they cause an energetic imbalance and consequently lead to an overcooling of the body. Girls and young women especially should avoid eating large quantities of fresh salad. The overcooling of their bodies can lead to fertility problems, difficulties with conceiving, miscarriages, premature births, weak and allergic children, problems with breastfeeding and early menopause.

Do not force your children to eat fresh salads (which they dislike anyway). Rather, they should eat vegetable soups or boiled and stewed vegetables as an addition to meals containing meat. From the earliest age, babies and children should be fed a variety of vegetables; do not hesitate to add cabbage, garlic, onion or some greens in their daily meals.

It is much more beneficial to our health to eat large quantities and variety of vegetables rather than fruit (especially tropical fruit). I do realize that it is much more convenient to give your child a banana (which you can even carry in your bag) rather than cook for them a tasty and nutritious soup.

One method of preserving vegetables is pickling. In this way, we can preserve vegetables such as cabbage, cucumbers, tomatoes, mushrooms and mixed vegetables.

In the old days, pickled vegetables used to be an important element of our winter diet. They were a substitute for fruit and a complementary source of the sour flavour. Sour flavour, used in moderation, strengthens the liver. However, too much of it can have the opposite effect. If we want to reduce the cooling nature of, for example, sauerkraut then we can do so by adding some spices (juniper berries, cumin, black pepper, ginger, turmeric) and/or some vegetables (carrots, onion and sweet cabbage).

Pickled gherkins are strongly cooling. They can have a damaging effect on the stomach, spleen, pancreas and kidneys, especially when there is a deficiency of Yang within the body. Thus, they should not be eaten too often. A slice of gherkin in your sandwich or one or two gherkins in your salad or sauce is acceptable. But if you eat too many pickled gherkins during the summer then you can be almost certain that you will have some health problems in the autumn and winter!

One of the most popular vegetables is tomato. Nowadays we eat tomatoes practically all year round. But I would rather recommend you ate tomatoes only in the summer and autumn, when this is the season for them. Vegetables grown in greenhouses merely destroy the order of nature. Fresh tomatoes are best with some onion, garlic and lots of warming spices. Tomatoes are also a great component of cooked (boiled or stewed) meals as they increase their taste and balance them with the sour flavour. Thus, small quantities of tomatoes in our cooked meals are acceptable throughout the whole year.

## Legumes

Legumes are highly nutritious. They are a great source of protein, B vitamins and very important mineral salts, such as calcium, phosphorus, magnesium and potassium.

**Split peas** are of a neutral and warming nature. They belong to the element of Earth. There is a common opinion that split peas are difficult to digest, but this is only true of people who suffer from a weak and cold stomach, spleen and intestines. Appropriately prepared and with the addition of certain spices, split peas are very good for you as they strengthen the element of Earth (kidneys) and boost your energy.

One of the most popular split pea dishes is split pea soup, usually based on a meat stock. We can make the soup easier to digest and absorb by adding some vegetables, onion and garlic, as well as some marjoram, turmeric, cumin, black and white pepper and ginger.

We should also balance the soup by adding some sour flavour (e.g. lemon juice). This small trick will prevent us from suffering problems with flatulence.

Split peas are good for everyone, but most of all they are very beneficial for children and the young.

Green peas are also very nutritious as they contain B vitamins and vitamins A, E and C. When they are in season we should try and eat them as often as possible. They go nicely in soups and stewed vegetable meals. In winter we can use canned peas instead (in cooked meals and salads) as they have a strengthening effect on the stomach and spleen.

**Broad beans** are of a neutral nature and belong to the element of Earth. We should eat them as often as possible because they are very nutritious and have a strengthening effect on the stomach, spleen and pancreas.

**Beans, lentils and soya beans** are of a cooling nature and belong to the element of Water.

Because of their cooling nature, we should eat beans mostly in the spring and summer. In order to make them easier to digest we can add large quantities of warming spices (much more than with split pea), such as marjoram, thyme, turmeric, cumin, black pepper, ginger, summer savory, but also onion and garlic. During winter, in order to increase our Yang, we should eat beans together with beef, veal or lamb. Beans are very good for strengthening the kidneys and therefore should be eaten by everyone, but most of all by children and the young.

Lentils possess similar properties to beans. They should be also prepared with the addition of onion, garlic and warming spices.

Remember not to mix beans, lentils and soya beans together with sauerkraut, cucumbers and fresh salads, as this kind of combination would have a strongly cooling and weakening effect on the body.

## Nuts

Nuts have a very condensed structure. They are a great source of protein, fat and, most of all, B vitamins and vitamins A and E, as well as mineral salts (calcium, phosphorus, magnesium, iron, sulphur and potassium).

Nuts strengthen the heart and blood circulation, lower cholesterol levels, and have an antioxidant and anti-cancer effect on the body. Eaten in moderation, they have a positive impact on our body, as they strengthen the stomach, spleen and pancreas, stimulate the production of internal bodily fluids and nourish the left kidney.

However, the energetic and nutritious value of nuts is so high that only a healthy body is able to digest and absorb it. If someone suffers from allergies, asthma, diabetes, obesity or stomach problems (weakness and overcooling symptoms), then nuts can only increase these health problems. Even a very strong and healthy body will not be able to cope with large quantities of nuts.

Nuts can increase the nutritious and energetic value of cooked food as well as cakes. However, one should always eat nuts in moderation.

Other very popular products such as sunflower seeds, linseed and sesame or pumpkin seeds should be treated and used in the same way as nuts. Small quantities of these seeds strengthen internal bodily fluids and, consequently, the whole body. However, eating too many seeds can weaken the spleen and stimulate an excessive production of moisture and mucus within the body. This can lead to problems with stalling of energy and weaken the blood circulation.

**Fruit**

Fruit is of a cooling and moist nature. It has a refreshing effect on the body. In our climatic zone, fruit plays a rather supplementary role in our diet (mostly in the summer); it is a seasonal occurrence and thus should be eaten only in season. Do not spoil the flavour of fruit by adding sugar, yogurts or milk! If you do not like it on its own, simply stop eating it. Also, do not force your children to eat raw fruit against their will. A mixture of fruit, sugar and dairy products has a strongly cooling nature and can have an acidifying and destructive effect on our body. This mixture is one of the causes of allergies.

We should eat fruit wisely and always take into consideration their nature (which in most cases is rather cooling). Most suitable for us is the fruit that grows in our own climate. Only our local fruit can be truly fresh and good for us.

All tropical fruits have a strongly refreshing and cooling effect on the body. This is because they are meant for a hot climate. Unfortunately, the tropical fruit we get to buy in our supermarkets is of a rather poor quality. It is usually collected before it is ripe, then covered in artificial preservatives for shipping and stored for months before reaching our local stores. Its nutritional value is rather doubtful. I especially do not recommend giving it to children!

We should remember that we live in a mild climatic zone with distinct seasonal change. Meat is available to us throughout the year, as are grains, beans and split pea. Fresh fruit, on the other hand, is available only during hot summer months and in early autumn. This is the time when we should eat ripe and sweet apples, pears and plums, because they are then of most value and nutrition. We should, however, avoid eating frozen fruit, fruit yogurts and tropical fruit. Autumn is the time of preparation for winter and we should not unnecessarily overcool our body. In winter, on the other hand, we should only eat food of a warming nature.

The so-called spring fatigue is in fact a result of the previous spring and summer's malnutrition as well as of the gluttony of Christmas. Instead of getting ready for the time of winter and storing the necessary energy, we often overcool our body by eating lots of fruit and drinking cold drinks. This leads to a deficiency of magnesium and A, D and B vitamins. And fruit, despite appearances, does not provide us with the required quantities of nutrients. In fact, an excess of fruit in our diet weakens and overcools our system.

We can decrease the cooling nature of fruit by cooking it (boiling or roasting in an oven) with the addition of such spices as cinnamon, ginger, cardamom, cloves and honey. We can also use some sweet and ripe fruit in homemade preserves, such as apricot, plum or pear jams, but we should only sweeten them with honey.

## Cereal

In our climate, cereals are the basic element of our daily diet. They provide us with carbohydrates, protein and important vitamins and mineral salts. We usually use them for making bread, grains and pasta. They are most beneficial, though, when chewed very slowly; this way they do not acidify our body!

## Bread

Bread can be identified as the centre of all food. It belongs to the element of Earth and contains large amounts of life energy. It is of a neutral sweet nature which strengthens all the bodily organs. It combines well with all food products. But we must remember that the types that are best for us are baked whole-flour breads (wheat or rye) with no artificial additives. A type that is especially good for our health is rye bread, which strengthens the heart, improves blood circulation and prevents blood clots.

Modern baking technologies enable the production of white and fluffy bread with lots of additives. However, this kind of bread is not of much value or benefit to our health. On an everyday basis, we should rather stick to the dark type of bread (whole-flour rye bread or sourdough bread). Eating large quantities of white bread can affect our stomach, intestines and liver. We should only have it from time to time, on special occasions, or when we suffer from liver fire. We should also remember that freshly baked bread is difficult to digest; therefore chew it properly. Whole-flour breads can also be quite heavy on the stomach, especially for those with a weakened and cold stomach, intestines and liver. If you suffer from any of these ailments, it does not mean that you have to give up eating bread completely. Simply reduce the portions and go for older bread rather than freshly baked.

Bread is a healthy and most universal food product. Good quality bread contains very important B vitamins, mineral salts (calcium, phosphorus, iron, magnesium) and fibre. The most important characteristic of bread is the fact that all of its nutrients are in perfect balance.

We should not follow new dietary fashions inducing us to stop eating bread or replace it with fresh salads. This can be quite dangerous for our health and especially for children and the young. Young people need bread for their proper development. That is why we should always remember to send them to school with a homemade sandwich. And this applies to younger kids as well as teenagers, who also need looking after.

Of recent popularity are breads made with a variety of seeds. These should not be eaten too often, and if consumed should be older rather than freshly baked. Eaten every day, they can lead to problems with the stomach and spleen, excessive production of mucus and stalling of energy.

## Pasta

Pasta is usually made with high gluten wheat flour. Gluten is a kind of protein that is difficult to digest as it absorbs water (up to twice its own mass) and becomes gooey and elastic. Thus, gluten is valuable only from the pasta producers' point of view. Within our body gluten causes a lot of damage. It is dangerous for children suffering from coeliac disease as much as it is for other people who overindulge in pasta and white bread. Gluten destroys and overcools the stomach, spleen, pancreas, intestines and liver.

Plain wheat flour has the same weakening, cooling and acidifying effect on the body as white rice and sugar. In order to mitigate the negative impact of pasta one should eat it with the addition of warming and strengthening spices, such as turmeric, ginger and cinnamon (spices which strongly strengthen the spleen, intestines and liver).

Pasta is very popular in modern cuisine because it is quick and easy to prepare. Therefore we eat it quite often. To avoid its cooling and weakening effect on the body we should serve it together with other food products. The best options are spicy vegetable sauces with the addition of onion, garlic, ginger, black pepper and cumin. Tomato sauces should be based on onion and garlic, with large quantities of added spices. With sweet sauces, on the other hand, we should add cinnamon, cardamom and cloves. Pasta should never be served together with sour sauces, fresh salads and chicken, as it then becomes strongly cooling. The basis of our diet should become grains and potatoes and not pasta!

**Grains**

Grains are easy to digest and absorb. They are a source of many valuable nutrients, such as B vitamins and mineral salts (mostly magnesium and calcium).

**Millet grains** are of a neutral warming nature and belong to the element of Earth. They have a strengthening effect on the stomach, spleen and pancreas. They also have alkaline properties, which are very important during recovery from cancer, which usually causes strong acidification of the body.

Millet grains strengthen a weak and overcooled body through an effective stimulation and nourishment of the element of Earth (kidneys). We can always increase the Yang (warmth) of millet grains by roasting them in a pan. They are especially beneficial for those who suffer from stomach, spleen, intestinal and kidney problems.

**Cornmeal** is of a slightly warming nature and belongs to the element of Earth. It strengthens the stomach, spleen, pancreas, intestines and kidneys. It is not as popular as other grains. Nevertheless, it goes well with meat-veg sauces and soups.

**Pearl barley** is of a neutral nature and belongs to the element of Metal. It has a strengthening effect on the stomach, spleen, intestines and kidneys. It cleanses the body from an excess of mucus and moisture and therefore is especially recommended for diabetics. It is commonly used as an addition to soups and meats.

**Porridge oats** are of a warming nature and belong to the element of Metal. They mostly strengthen the kidneys, but also the stomach, spleen and intestines. They increase physical strength and energy within the body. They also stimulate the appetite, reduce cholesterol levels, detoxify nicotine, balance emotions and help with diarrhoea.

**White rice** is of a cooling nature and belongs to the element of Metal. Like pasta, it should be served together with spicy meat-veg sauces. Turmeric, ginger and other warming spices decrease the cooling nature of white rice. A similar effect can be achieved by mixing white rice with pearl barley or buckwheat (in the ratio 1:1). We should always add some cinnamon to sweet rice dishes!

**Brown rice** is of a warming nature and belongs to the element of Metal. It is very good for strengthening the stomach, spleen, kidneys and lungs. Despite all of its goodness and nutritional value, it is still seldom used in our cuisine.

**Wheat grains** are of a cooling nature and belong to the element of Wood. They are not very popular in our cuisine. Nevertheless, I do recommend wheat grains for their strengthening and nutritional properties.

Whole-wheat grains have a purifying and medicinal effect, especially on those who suffer from liver and heart fire. In spring we can introduce a special kind of diet which lasts for twelve days and is based on eating only cooked whole-wheat grains and drinking parsley tea. This diet is rather difficult to complete, but the final effect is definitely worth the sacrifice.

**Semolina** is a cereal food made from wheat grains. It is of a cooling nature, and therefore we should not eat too much of it. It is best with some turmeric and cinnamon! Semolina is often given to babies, which goes against common sense, as it contains large quantities of gluten and has a strongly cooling effect on a baby's body. I would suggest taking semolina off a baby's diet or at least mixing it together with meat-veg soups. Semolina is not good for old people either. I would suggest replacing it with some gruel based on pearl barley, oats, cornmeal or millet grains.

**Buckwheat** is of a warming nature and belongs to the element of Fire. It strengthens the spleen and kidneys and strongly warms up the body. That is why we should eat it more often in autumn and winter as an addition to meat-veg stews. In the summer, on the other hand, we can eat it together with beans, lentils and sour milk. Because of its specific taste, buckwheat is not everyone's favourite. However, by mixing it with some rice we can improve the taste and make it more appealing to children. Cabbage rolls stuffed with buckwheat, rice and meat, mixed together with onion and spices, are very tasty.

We should introduce grains into our diet very early in life. However, babies should not be given semolina, as mixed together with milk and sugar it can cause an acidifying and overcooling effect on their body. Instead we can give them all the other kinds of grains, ground in a grinder and mixed together with milk or soups. I especially recommend millet grains, cornmeal and oats.

## Cakes and biscuits

All cakes are of a cooling nature and have a weakening effect on the stomach, spleen and pancreas. However, if our diet is well balanced, two small biscuits with a cup of coffee a day will not do us any harm. Sweets are also good but only in moderation.

The best ones for us are shortcrust pastry cakes and biscuits baked with the addition of saffron, turmeric, cinnamon and cloves. We can also bake them with some added dried fruit, nuts, seeds, jams or even fresh fruit. Among all bakery products, these cakes and biscuits have the least cooling effect on the body and the spleen in particular.

I do not recommend creamy cakes with fresh fruit, whipped cream or jelly because all of these products can only increase the cooling nature of a cake. Such a mix can strongly weaken our body. However, a birthday cake made according to the rule of Five Flavours and with the addition of the appropriate spices (and eaten in moderation) should not cause any problems.

Yeast cakes are thought to be easy to digest and low in calories. However, such ingredients as white flour, milk, sugar and yeast are highly cooling and acidifying. All of them mixed together weaken and destroy the intestines and liver. In order to reduce the negative properties of yeast cakes we should bake them together with egg yolks, butter, saffron, turmeric, cinnamon or ginger. This type of yeast cake will add a nice variety to our daily menu.

There are a few things we should always remember about cakes. Never mix cakes and biscuits with cold drinks! Do not eat cakes and fresh fruit together! If you decide to eat a slice of cake, then never mix it with ice cream! Eating cakes before dinner will affect our digestion! Do not eat cakes if you are planning to eat meat or fish afterwards! Cakes are better eaten in the summer than in winter (additional overcooling)! We should always serve cakes with hot drinks, such as anise tea or chicory coffee for children, and boiled natural coffee for adults!

**Sugar and sweets**

Sugar is a chemically purified, sweet-flavoured substance. It is commonly referred to as the 'white poison' or *empty calories*. The most common sugar of all is sucrose; it is a disaccharide obtained from sugar cane or sugar beet.

Sugar is very bad for our health. It is of a cooling nature, strongly acidifies the body, weakens the spleen, stomach and liver and stimulates an excessive production of mucus. Because of its cooling and moistening properties, sugar is best for people living in a hot climate.

An intense craving for sugar and sweets is usually a symptom of an imbalance in the functioning of the stomach, spleen and pancreas. It also means that these particular bodily organs, which belong to the element of Earth and play a very important regulatory role within the body, are significantly weakened and overcooled. In order to function properly, they need the natural kind of sweetness. Craving for sweets may also be a symptom of problems with heat within the body (fire).

Natural sources of sugar and sweet flavour include vegetable and meat-veg dishes, eggs, butter, honey, nuts, grains, cereal, potatoes and liquorice.

When a craving for sweets and sugar occurs, we should reduce the consumption of sour food, fruit, fresh salads, cold drinks and ice cream, because all of these products weaken the stomach, spleen and pancreas and thus make the situation even worse for us. The only way to get rid of the addiction to sugar is to warm up the spleen by eating cooked and warm food.

We should not mix sugar with milk and other dairy products, nor with fruit, fruit juices or raw vegetables. Otherwise we can experience problems with the digestion and absorption of nutrients, as well as augmenting the state of overcooling within the body. Eating large amounts of sweets damages bodily organs to the point where they can no longer digest and absorb such basic products as vegetables, grains or meat. As a consequence, it can lead to the destruction of the body. We can observe this in children who eat lots of sweets and yogurts and drink cold and sweet drinks or fruit juices. They usually have problems with appetite and cannot even force themselves to eat their dinner completely.

Children do need the sweet flavour for their proper growth and development. However, it must not be provided by sugar! Sugar can only ruin their health!

Sugar also means sweets. Even ingredients such as flour, milk, fat, cocoa, nuts or fruit, often found in sweets, will not neutralize the damaging impact of sugar. In fact, they will only augment it. We do not need sweets at all because they destroy the body and are especially bad for children and the young. I personally think that advertisements of sweets or ice cream are fundamentally immoral, because they encourage the destruction of one's own health. The consumption of sweets by children should always occur under the supervision of adults. Excessive consumption of sweets can deregulate the functioning of the young child and lead to most of the childhood diseases and disorders observed. This in turn, as a consequence, can cause even more serious problems in adulthood (allergies, anaemia, chronic colds, asthma, diabetes, obesity, etc.).

We do not need to be rid of sweets completely, but merely need to eat them in moderation. For example, chocolate eaten in excess becomes a poison, but two or three pieces of chocolate will not do any harm. Chocolate is made of a milk and sugar concentrate mixed together with fat and cocoa. It is heavy on the stomach and, like other sweets, has a cooling effect on the body.

## Drinks

**Water.** A well-balanced body self-regulates the required amount of its internal fluids. In order to sustain the balance, an average human body needs to receive and excrete the same amount of fluids per day. We need on average 2.5l of water a day, of which 1.2l are all types of drinks, 1l comes from food and 0.3l is a by-product of chemical processes that occur within the body. To keep the balance, we need to give away 2.5l of water: 1.4l in urine, 0.5l in sweat, 0.2l in faeces and 0.4l through our lungs. The balance needs to stay even!

Upsetting this balance can lead to all sorts of health problems or even death.

If we provide too much water to our body (more than it can cope with) then the excess of water feeds the extracellular fluid, and this is the most common reason for swelling. Some of this water may also be stored within the body's cavities and lead to e.g. pleural effusion.

**The popular recommendations by doctors and dieticians, who say that in order to cleanse and hydrate our body we should drink 2.5–3l per day, can in fact be very dangerous. We are not some sort of pump or a machine**

**that one can swamp with water**. The excess of water is hard on the heart and kidneys. Besides, we should remember that water, as much as any other food we put into our mouth, is of a specific nature. In this case it is of a cooling nature. Thus by consuming an excessive quantity of water, we run the risk of overcooling our body.

Drinking cold water in a hot climate makes sense. In our climate, we should be careful with cold drinks even during the summer. Instead, we need something to strengthen and warm us up.

Where does the fashion for drinking large amounts of water come from? I really do not know. Maybe we simply lack common sense? Just because somebody else is drinking a lot of water does not necessarily mean that it will be good for us, too.

Drinking water was and is a very important element of Eastern culture. For example, yogis, who pay considerable attention to the so-called energizing of the body, drink fresh spring water in small sips, holding each sip in their mouth for about 30sec., mixing it with saliva and warming it up to the temperature of their body. This way of drinking water is so different from the 'rinsing' of the body with large amounts of water so popular nowadays in Western culture. One should also remember that our physiology precludes detoxifying with water.

If we want to get rid of the unnecessary substances from our body we have to make sure that it is strong enough and has the right vibration, i.e. sufficient warmth, effective digestion and absorption, good circulation, no breathing or excretion problems, and the right quality and quantity of blood. Drinking lots of water will not make these complex processes more efficient. It can actually do the opposite because, due to its cooling nature, water slows down cellular metabolism.

Drinking large amounts of water can be very harmful, especially during a starvation diet, because it causes an excessive overcooling of the body. One should drink instead appropriate herbal teas. Also, drinking water before, during, or after a meal, can drastically decrease the digestive capability of the stomach and spleen.

If we want to create the so-called energizing effect of drinking water on our body, we should follow the example of yogis. People who eat large quantities of meat (60% of their diet or more) have a greater need for water than those with a balanced diet.

What then should we do in the summer when it is very hot?

Many of us have probably noticed that the more cold drinks or fruit juices we drink, or ice cream that we eat, the thirstier we feel. We sweat more, and we feel weaker and less resistant to the heat. Thus, perhaps counterintuitively, we should rather drink hot, boiled coffee and hot herbal teas as well as black or green tea with a touch of honey. We should do so slowly, in small sips; only in this way will we be able to quench our thirst. I do also recommend lukewarm chicory or natural coffee. It is impossible to quench one's thirst with juices or water.

The feeling of thirst occurs when there is a deficiency of internal bodily fluids, which are normally produced by the spleen. When we drink too many cold, sour or sweet drinks and eat too much food of a similar nature, the spleen becomes too weak and too cold to keep up with the production of fluids. On the other hand, excessive sweating can be a symptom of a weak heart or lungs.

If we drink large amounts of cold drinks during the summer, then in the autumn, winter and spring we can expect certain health problems. Most of the time we do not realize the connection between our summer diet and the illnesses we get later in the year.

Remember that water belongs to the element of Water and drunk in excess it will destroy your kidneys, liver, heart and spleen, but most of all it will extinguish your life fire.

**Juices.** Why can juices be dangerous for us?

There are two types of juice available on the market. The first type contains 100% pure fruit juice, which means that, for example, one box of orange juice is the equivalent of eating 1kg of oranges. The other type is a mixture of water, fruit concentrate and sugar. The first type is dangerous because drinking one or two boxes of orange juice a day is the equivalent of eating one or two kilograms of oranges. And this is far too much for our body to cope with, and thus very bad for our health. The second type of fruit juice is not healthy because of its doubtful ingredients (especially sugar).

Let's talk about natural (100%) homemade juices. By eating whole fruit we provide our body not only with the juice but also fibre; we bite the fruit, we chew on it slowly and the juice dilutes in our saliva (this is when the digestion process begins). Also, this way we do not exceed the quantity of fruit that is beneficial to our health, as we are simply not able to eat more than, for example, two apples and a carrot at a time. For making juices, in contrast, we use larger quantities of fruit; instead of two apples we use 1kg of apples, and at the end of the process we often add some sugar as well. By drinking too much of these juices, without chewing and mixing it with saliva, we put too much pressure on the stomach, spleen and intestines. As a result, this leads to acidification of the body and very low absorption of vitamins.

Fruit juices are believed to be rich in multivitamins. But the fact is that there are not as many vitamins in fruit juices as we think and they are usually difficult to digest, especially when we suffer from the effects of a cold gastrointestinal tract. Juices merely stimulate the production of mucus and moisture within the body. Consumed systematically in large amounts they have a cooling and weakening effect on the body and destroy the stomach, spleen and intestines.

Vegetable juices have a similar effect on our body. For example, carrot juice, even though it is sweet, consumed in large amounts can weaken the spleen and block the liver because of its high carotene content. Beetroot juice, on the other hand, is bitter-sweet and has a cooling effect on the body; consumed in large amounts it can damage the intestines. Celeriac juice is refreshing and strongly diuretic, but it has a weakening effect on the spleen and kidneys. In general, fruit and vegetable juices should be consumed in small amounts and diluted in water (at a ratio of 1:1). They should be drunk in the morning, very slowly, in small sips and should be mixed properly with saliva!

In certain situations, juices can help with the ailments of our body. We should think of them then as a kind of medicine and use them only for the duration of the treatment.

**Tea.** China is the motherland of tea. The tradition of drinking tea there goes back to 3000 BC. In Europe, people started drinking tea in the 18th century. Tea does not contain any vitamins or mineral salts. Instead it contains oxalates, oxalic acid and purines (about 170 times more than broths based on bones and meat). Oxalates block the absorption of many nutrients, such as magnesium, calcium, iron and zinc.

Tea is commonly thought to be of a neutral nature. Whilst it does indeed have a refreshing and cooling effect on the body, tea is of a bitter flavour; it dries out and acidifies the body, and has diuretic properties. Tea drunk in large amounts can have a drying effect on the skin and hair. Tea with sugar is used in Arab countries as a strongly cooling drink. Therefore, drinking black tea with sugar and lemon as a remedy for colds or flus can be very dangerous.

Tea is a remedy for the liver and heart fire. It also helps to deal with the effects of eating too much beef or lamb and detoxifies the body from alcohol. Chinese people drink mostly green tea for the purpose of balancing the strongly warming food they eat (Chinese cuisine is famous for its spices and composition of flavours). Thanks to their special diet, Chinese people do not suffer from high cholesterol levels. This has nothing to do with drinking green tea but with the compositionally well-balanced diet.

Green tea in our climatic and cultural reality simply does not pass the test. It was introduced in the hope that it would lower cholesterol levels or stimulate metabolism, but in fact in our climatic zone is totally ineffective. Do not forget that our cuisine is mostly of a cooling nature. Green tea removed from its 'Chinese context' does not work the way most doctors and dieticians would expect it to work.

We should thus take into consideration the true nature of tea. It is a popular and well-loved drink; however, we should drink it in moderation and at the right time of the year. I do not recommend tea to children, the young or those who suffer a deficiency of Yang in their stomach and spleen.

**Herbal teas.** Many dieticians recommend drinking herbal teas (especially to older people). I am convinced that we would drink more of them if only we know their properties. Some of them are cooling; some of them are neutral or warming. Like any other food product, they are of a specific nature. So, for example:

- Peppermint tea is strongly cooling; it is a great remedy for liver fire; however, drunk in excess it can weaken the liver and affect our sight.

- Camomile tea is of a cooling nature; the warmth we get from it is deceptive and lasts as long as we are drinking it; it is a good remedy for inflammation.

- Thyme tea is of a warming nature; especially recommended to deal with an excess of moisture and the effects of overcooling within the body.

- Aniseed tea is of a neutral nature and has a calming and anti-cramping effect on the body.

- Lime flower tea is of a warming and neutral nature.

- Sour fruit tea is cooling and refreshing.

- Black tea with the addition of jasmine flowers is strongly warming.

- Liquorice tea is of a neutral nature, sweet flavour and has balancing and anti-cancer properties; it strengthens the immune system; it is very much recommended.

- Ginger tea is of a strongly warming nature; it is very good for the liver-stomach stalling, but also for flatulence and vomiting.

- Lemon balm tea has calming properties.

- Marigold flower tea is of a neutral and strengthening nature.

The most beneficial for our health are mixed teas made of three to five different herbs. For example:

- Thyme + liquorice + ginger = warming properties.

- Sour fruit + thyme + aniseed + liquorice + ginger = neutral properties.

- Dates + liquorice + cinnamon + ginger = warming properties.

- Thyme + liquorice + peppermint = cooling properties.

- Camomile + liquorice + peppermint = cooling and anti-cramp properties.

- Thyme + lime flower + liquorice = warming.

- Sour fruit + thyme + lime flower + liquorice + ginger = neutral.

Liquorice is one of the most important herbs for strengthening the element of Earth (spleen, pancreas and stomach). It is a misconception that liquorice increases blood pressure. This would only happen if we used too much of it or without the addition of other herbs. Well balanced with other herbs, it does not cause any side effects.

**Coffee.** The motherland of coffee is Abyssinia (modern Ethiopia). The peoples of Abyssinia have drunk coffee for centuries and always with the addition of butter and salt.

Coffee, like tea, does not have any nutritional value. It contains caffeine, which is synthesized from purine. Caffeine has a specific effect on the body. Therefore we should drink coffee in moderation, only a few cups per day.

There are two ways of preparing coffee. We can either brew or boil it. Brewed coffee has a different nature to boiled coffee. Some people claim that brewed coffee rids one of tiredness, stimulates one intellectually, brightens up the mind and broadens one's imagination. However, the majority of people after drinking brewed coffee may experience such side effects as anxiety, a faster heartbeat, dizziness, insomnia and a strained nervous system. It can also cause certain dysfunctions within the gastrointestinal tract and lead to an acidification of the body.

A bad tolerance to brewed coffee is especially characteristic of those suffering from hyperacidity, peptic ulcers, hyperactivity, insomnia, as well as a weakened spleen, liver, kidneys or intestines. Brewed coffee is also not advisable for people suffering from the liver and heart fire or high blood pressure.

Filtered coffee is not as strong as brewed coffee, does not make us hyperactive, and does not cause the sensations.

Boiled coffee, on the other hand, has a completely different nature and flavour to brewed coffee; it is milder and 'softer'. Using the same quantity of ground coffee, boiled coffee gives the impression of being much weaker than brewed or filtered coffee. Some people claim that the boiling process neutralizes caffeine. Boiled coffee is of a warming nature. It stimulates the whole body and especially the kidneys.

It stimulates metabolism, soothes the effects of tiredness and rheumatic pains, eliminates migraines and premenstrual syndrome, and is well tolerated by those suffering from heartburn and peptic ulcers. It does not aggravate the nervous system nor cause any problems with the heart. Boiled coffee is very good for allergies, asthma, coughs, colds and a weakened spleen and stomach. We can increase its warming nature by adding, whilst boiling, some cinnamon, cardamom or ginger. Boiled coffee does not have an acidifying effect on the body.

A morning cup of boiled coffee stimulates the kidneys. However, we should always add a touch of honey to it (bitter coffee can block the liver). The best honey in this case is mild or neutral honey, such as oilseed rape honey or multi-floral honey. We should never drink coffee with solid food, as we may experience digestive problems.

We should also not add milk to boiled coffee, as it is already 'soft'. Many experts claim that adding cream or milk to coffee affects its digestion.

**Chicory coffee** is also very popular. Hot chicory coffee has warming properties. Cold chicory coffee, on the other hand, has cooling properties and is especially recommended for those labouring in hot weather conditions. It is also very good for children, much better than tea, which has a cooling effect on the body and contains alkaloids. We should include chicory coffee in our everyday diet and drink it for breakfast and supper. You can drink it with some honey or milk.

**Cocoa** is valued for its flavour and magnesium content. Native Americans used to boil cocoa with some added vanilla and cayenne pepper. Because of its strongly warming properties, they called it 'the drink of life'. It helped them survive the harshness of the climate.

Nowadays we mostly drink cocoa with milk and sugar, both of which are strongly cooling and cause allergic reactions. It is much better to mix cocoa with water and boil it for a few minutes, adding some cinnamon and honey. This kind of drink has warming and strengthening properties. On the other hand, cold cocoa drinks have a cooling effect on the body.

**Fruit compotes** are of a strongly cooling nature. Those made from sour and unripe fruit, and with the addition of large amounts of sugar, have an especially bad impact on our health as they cool the stomach, spleen and intestines. Drinking compotes with meals slows down the digestive process. We should drink fruit compotes rarely because they unnecessarily cool our body.

Instead, we can make a very similar drink but of a completely different nature. We need only boil some sweet and ripe fruit (use a mixture of different fruit) with the addition of cinnamon, cloves, ginger and honey. This type of compote is highly energetic and at the same time very refreshing, thus great for hot summer days (however, it should always be drunk lukewarm). We can also turn it into a very nutritious jelly by simply adding some gelatine. However, as with other food products, we should drink/eat it in moderation. Boiled fruit from the compote can be used as a remedy for a high temperature, for it is very refreshing.

I will not say much about cola and other fizzy sugary drinks because every reasonable person knows that they are very bad health-wise. They are strongly overcooling; they destroy the whole gastrointestinal tract and weaken the spleen, liver and kidneys. It is acceptable to drink them sporadically; however, one should not be surprised at any atypical and unpleasant reaction to those drinks.

General rules about drinks:

- Avoid cold drinks or drinks with ice added.

- We are supposed to 'chew on' drinks, i.e. mix each sip thoroughly with saliva.

- Avoid drinking cold drinks before, during and after meals and before going to bed.

- The more cold drinks we drink, the thirstier and weaker we become and we sweat even more.

- Avoid 100% fruit juices.

**Beer.** One can say that advertising campaigns for beer are as big as those for fruit yogurts. But the fact is that both of these products make us feel bad. Thus, do not follow this false marketing!

We should look at it from a certain perspective, gain some distance towards modern fashions and learn more about our dietary traditions, because they are a great source of knowledge.

Dieticians and medical doctors put beer in the same category as other alcoholic drinks. But the fact is that it is sometimes better for us to have a shot of vodka instead of two or three beers. We reach a similar level of tipsiness, yet the damage done to our body is much smaller.

So, what is the truth about beer?

Beer is of a bitter flavour and of a strongly cooling nature. Thus, chilling beer before drinking it merely augments its cooling properties. A pint of beer from time to time (but not together with food) can be rather refreshing and invigorating, especially in the summer. However, if drinking beer turns into a daily habit and we keep having two or three bottles a day, then it becomes dangerous to our health.

Beer, next to milk and fizzy sugary drinks, is one of the most acidifying drinks. It causes heartburn and irritates peptic ulcers. Its cooling nature weakens the stomach and destroys the spleen, and it also ruins the intestines, heart, liver and kidneys, in that order. Overindulgence in beer leads to strokes and arteriosclerosis. This is because beer reduces the magnesium level within the body. Beer can also cause pancreatic cancer as well as cancer of the large intestine.

It is rather harmful to drink beer together with food. And men often do it; they eat fattening and highly calorific food and drink beer at the same time! Some of the meats, and especially pork (I mentioned this earlier in the book), are of a highly cooling nature. Thus, when we eat fatty pork with the addition of the wrong kind of spices and at the same time drink beer, our stomach is in a hopeless situation.

The cause of obesity among beer lovers is not just due to too much liquid, but most of all due to problems with digestion and metabolism (a weak spleen and stomach), as well as problems with blood circulation and the kidneys. Their bodies, despite their outer appearance (they usually look as if they are too hot), are usually overcooled.

I would also not recommend drinking large amounts of beer when trying to 'rinse' the sand from your kidneys, unless we do it whilst taking a hot bath, which is supposed to warm and loosen up the muscles of our urinary tract.

Beer can be a medicine sometimes! It is very good for heart fire, but only when accompanied by boiled wheat grains with natural yogurt. We should apply this diet for twelve days (best in this case is beer made out of wheat).

Warmed-up beer mixed together with ginger and honey is great for gloomy autumnal or cold wintery evenings.

**Wine.** Dry red wine belongs to the element of Fire (bitter flavour). It is usually served at room temperature and therefore does not cause excessive overcooling. It stimulates metabolism and helps with the digestion of meat. It does, however, have acidifying properties and is not suitable for those who suffer from hyperacidity or peptic ulcers. Excessive consumption of red wine can also weaken the stomach and spleen. French people, who keep having more and more health problems (cirrhosis, which is an effect of a cold liver, has become one of the most common diseases within French society) have started to acknowledge that drinking wine during meals may be one of the reasons for it. They have tried to reduce the consumption of wine and replaced it with water. However, this is not the main reason for their health problems. I would say that it is rather their overindulgence in cheeses, green salads, fruit and cold food that causes most of their health problems. Drinking water only makes the whole situation even worse.

Red wine can have a medicinal effect on the body. Drinking 0.5l of red wine mixed with egg yolks a day can increase the quality and quantity of blood. We can also drink it with the addition of certain spices (cinnamon, ginger, etc.); it is then highly warming and therefore great for long wintery evenings. Red wine is usually associated with elegance, luxury and health, and I do agree with this opinion. I recommend drinking wine for any special occasion or celebration. It is much better than cold beer, water or cola or other fizzy drink.

Dry white wine belongs to the element of Wood. It is of a slightly sour flavour and has a refreshing, but overcooling, effect on the body. According to the common rule, white wine goes best with white meats, such as chicken and fish. Thus, in order to keep the balance, I would recommend eating something warming after this type of meal.

**Strong alcohols.** Cognac and whisky are of a warming and stimulating nature. It is advisable to have a shot of either of them to brighten one's mood, improve blood circulation or warm up. They are not as acidifying as beer or wine. Vodka, for example, helps to unload stress, stimulate a blocked liver, digest an excess of meat and improves one's mood and wellbeing. Naturally, I am talking here about one or two shots, not more. Excessive drinking of vodka can destroy the stomach, lungs, liver and, most of all, one's own character, devastating one's consciousness and subconscious.

The cause of alcoholism is not alcohol as such, but dietary and emotional problems (mostly within the family). In the previous chapter, I mentioned that bad dietary habits can lead to formation of certain behavioural models, which result in all sorts of emotional problems, phobias, psychic weakness and lack of determination for solving everyday problems.

There are various problems pushing people towards alcohol. These might be financial problems, customary or cultural problems, as well as all sorts of complexes. A physically and emotionally strong person does not seek ways of escaping reality; they simply know that it is impossible to drown one's own problems with alcohol. Alcoholism can arise when the body lacks balance and physical strength. One can observe that even a genius, just as much as someone from the bottom of society, can easily turn into an alcoholic. Very often alcoholism is associated with those people who eat excessive quantities of pork, sea fish and salt.

Pork, and especially ham and sausages, eaten in excess can cause blockages in the flow of energy (stalling). It is very hard on the stomach, spleen, liver and kidneys, and usually causes some emotional problems (depression, phobias, etc.). Alcohol is of strongly warming properties, thus helps to move the energy and unblock the emotional tensions within the body. Alcohol can also help to brighten the mood of malnourished and overstressed people (it increases their Yang). However, it is not a solution to their personal problems.

In order to fight alcoholism, one needs to be very self-motivated, both physically (change of diet and lifestyle) and emotionally. Some people do succeed! And we can and should always try to help them, too.

**Fats**

Fats are an indispensable element in the process of metabolism; they enable the proper functioning of the stomach, spleen and pancreas. They are also a great source of essential vitamins. Together with other products from the element of Earth, such as vegetables, grains and meat, they regulate the appropriate amount and quality of internal fluids, which then nourish other bodily organs (especially the kidneys).

Fats are also indispensable in the process of growth and development, especially during puberty. A fat-free diet can cause serious hormonal imbalance in girls. And remember that we usually compensate for a lack of fats in our diet by consuming an excessive amount of sweets!

Fats can be dangerous to those suffering from the effects of a cold stomach, pancreas, spleen, intestines and liver. This applies mostly to people eating large quantities of fresh salads, sauerkraut, pickled gherkins, fruit and cheeses, as well as drinking lots of fruit juices. A combination of the sour flavour and fat is very dangerous for the body! Mixing sour and fatty foods should be avoided especially by those suffering from allergies, asthma, diabetes, obesity and people susceptible to heart attacks and liver disorders. In these cases, problems with the digestion and absorption of fat may occur, which only exacerbates the weakening of the spleen and pancreas and leads to stalling of energy. The only way to combat this situation is to warm up the body, but not with a fat-free diet, which can only escalate the problem.

## Vegetable fats

Olive oil belongs to the element of Earth (the same as the other vegetable oils). It is the healthiest of all of the vegetable oils and contains the most beneficial combination of unsaturated fatty acids. It can be used hot for frying, stewing and boiling as well as being served cold in salads and mayonnaise. Olive oil lowers cholesterol levels and blood pressure. It also regulates the level of sugar in blood and has a strongly antioxidant effect on the body. The most beneficial olive oil to our health is the extra virgin cold-pressed olive oil. However, as this is normally very expensive, there is a tendency to replace it with other, cheaper vegetable oils.

Soya bean and rapeseed oils are usually used for frying.

Sunflower seed, maize and peanut oils are great for stewing, boiling and go nicely in salads and mayonnaise. However, they are not suitable for frying at hot temperatures.

Linseed oil goes well with white cheeses and potatoes but should only be used cold. It contains the highest ratio of EFAs (essential fatty acids) and has medicinal properties, especially with skin and joint problems.

Using only vegetable oils in cooking can lead to a deficiency of vitamin E within the body. If such a situation occurs then it is advisable to eat more vegetables and grains. Maize and wheat-germ oils are the only oils containing vitamin E.

## Animal fats

Butter is of a neutral nature and belongs to the element of Earth. It is the most valuable of all fats, especially when eaten cold. It contains precious A, D,

E and B vitamins as well as mineral salts (phosphorus, potassium, calcium and magnesium). Butter should be eaten daily by everyone, and especially so by children and the young. It should also always accompany hard and white cheeses, as vitamin D enables the absorption of calcium. For the same reason, butter should always be added to beans, stewed vegetables and even bone stocks.

Hot milk with the addition of butter and honey has strengthening and calming properties; it is advisable to give it to children before bed time. It is also a great remedy for colds and coughs. Butter does not increase cholesterol levels! Cholesterol level depends on completely different factors, such as bad metabolism, a deficiency of magnesium or overcooling of the body. Butter is especially good in osteoporosis because of the vitamins it contains (A, D and E).

Butter simply cannot be replaced by anything, not even by the best of margarines.

**Lard**, as pork, is probably of a cooling nature. Therefore it should be treated similarly to pork. In our climate, lard is especially beneficial for us in autumn and winter; it balances the Yang of the body.

Eating large quantities of lard and fatty meats without the addition of appropriate spices, and mixing them together with sour and raw foods or cold drinks and sweets, can cause many health problems. This kind of diet leads to blockages in the flow of energy and blood and an excessive production of mucus. However, lard is not the major cause of this situation but rather it is the additional food products which cause cooling.

Lard, eaten in moderation and with the appropriate spices, can improve our physical strength. It is especially good for the young. Mixed together with onion and some warming spices, it goes nicely with bread. It is also advisable to mix lard with grains, potatoes and lentils, but always remembering to add some warming spices.

**Goose fat** is of a neutral nature and belongs to the element of Earth. Like any other poultry fat, it regulates the cholesterol levels within the body. It is a very tasty and healthy addition to bread and various meals.

Another very important kind of fat is **fish-liver oil**. It is more of a medicine than a food product. It contains large quantities of vitamin A, D and E. There is no other product with a similar concentration of these vitamins. Besides, cod-liver oil contains Omega-3 (one of the fatty acids), which has a wonderful effect on our body. Fish fats prevent blood clots, have anti-inflammatory properties, and help with diabetes, rheumatism, asthma, high blood pressure and psoriasis. Generally speaking, they improve the functioning of the element of Earth (stomach, spleen, pancreas), which means a better metabolism and stronger organism. Instead of drinking the rather nasty-tasting cod-liver oil, I recommend eating some fatty sea fish, such as salmon, mackerel, sardines, tuna, herring or halibut, 2–3 times a week.

**Herbs and spices**

Spices are an indispensable element of what we eat. They play the function of a catalyst, enabling easier and more efficient digestion and absorption. They are of a warming nature and usually have bitter, sweet and spicy flavours.

**Bitter flavour** = saffron and turmeric.

**Sweet flavour** = fennel, aniseed, cumin, juniper berries, cinnamon, sweet paprika and vanilla.

**Spicy flavour** = black, green, white and cayenne pepper, chilli, hot paprika, ginger, nutmeg, allspice, cardamom, bay leaves, cloves, nigella, curry powder, coriander and mustard seeds.

The beneficial influence of spices on the human body has been known for centuries. They have antiviral, antibacterial, painkilling and anti-inflammatory properties, help in the prevention of blood clots, heart attacks, diabetes and peptic ulcers, effectively lower blood pressure and cholesterol levels, and are strongly antioxidant, stimulating the endocrine system and strengthening the immune system.

When suffering from the heat conditions (liver, heart or lung fire), one must be careful with adding spices. If we accidentally use too much spice in food, then we can balance the overly warmed-up body by drinking some water with lemon or sour milk or having some white cheese.

Spices bring out the warming nature of food. Because most food products are of a cooling or neutral nature, we can warm them up by adding some spices or through the cooking process.

Using spices will become easier for us once we get to know and understand the classification of different spices according to the Five Elements Theory.

Different meats, and especially pork, poultry and fish, require spices the most; for example, ginger and all kinds of pepper reduce their cooling nature.

Herbs acquire a warming nature only through the process of cooking. Every respectful culinary tradition uses this method to increase (by adding herbs) the quality and taste of food, as well as ease the digestion process. They can be used with many various food products but mostly with meat. Dry herbs sprinkled on top of a ready meal do not have the warming properties and do not work in the same way as they would if cooked. The most recommended herbs are basil, marjoram, thyme, sage, rosemary, tarragon and garden savory.

We should get our children accustomed to eating herbs in food from an early age. The most beneficial spices for them are aniseed, fennel and cumin.

# BALANCED NUTRITION

*Let food be thy medicine and medicine be thy food.*

(Hippocrates)

**The main principle of a balanced nutrition is to strengthen and protect all of the bodily organs. Unbalanced nutrition, scarce in some flavours, creates excesses or deficiencies within particular bodily organs and leads to particular illnesses.**

Each one of the flavours is either Yin or Yang. Thus we should compose them in such a way that they suit our body's needs. In our climatic zone, we require the warming type of food throughout the whole year. An excess of a particular flavour in our diet (unbalanced nutrition), e.g. sweet flavour, deregulates the functioning of the stomach, spleen and pancreas, affects metabolism and the immune system, and weakens the kidneys and endocrine system. An excess of the sour flavour destroys the liver and weakens the spleen, pancreas and kidneys.

Destruction of our organism caused by malnutrition is a long-lasting and hidden process. The symptoms usually occur when a disease is already at an advanced stage. Our body often sends us signals about the imbalance within our body, but we usually ignore them or do not identify them in time. We also never associate them with our dietary mistakes. By introducing a balanced nutrition we automatically open our consciousness to all signs from within our body as well as from our environment. A well-balanced and sensitive organism is able to make the right choices. And this rule applies to all spheres of human life.

The major rule in the preparation of food is to follow the order of Five Flavours as well as the Yin-Yang theory (see Fig. 11, p.57).

In order to do this we need to learn about the flavours of particular food products and apply them according to the order of the Five Flavours in our meals.

In practice, this means that we should create our meals by adding particular food products (flavours) in a specific order.

In the case of boiling or stewing, we add the following ingredients at 1-minute intervals. Ingredients of the same flavour can be added at the same time. If we have to add some more spices to our meal, we should never rearrange the order of the Five Flavours and add pinches of all the missing spices. For example: a soup still needs some salt and pepper, even though we have already finished adding all the necessary ingredients, ending with the greenery (sour flavour); in this situation, we should first add some boiling water or thyme (bitter flavour) and some butter or cumin (sweet flavour); only after that can we add the necessary amount of salt and pepper.

It is not that important which flavour we start cooking with. But usually it is the bitter flavour (boiling water) both in soups and stewed meals, or the sweet flavour when we start with meat (fat). The overall properties of the meal depend on the final flavour. If we add pepper at the end of cooking then our meal will acquire the nature of the element of Metal (lungs and large intestine). If we add some greenery to a soup at the end, then it will acquire the energy and nature of the element of Wood (liver). All these rules apply to those meals that are initially well balanced with all flavours and which strengthen not only those elements ascribed to them (particular bodily organs) but the whole body too.

When there is only one dominant flavour in our meal, we will not be able to balance out its original nature even by following the rules of the Five Flavours order. But at least we will make it easier to digest and absorb. For example, we cannot get rid of the cooling nature of such food products as sauerkraut, sorrel soup, tomato soup, sweet cakes, pasta and cheeses. By adding certain products and spices we can only reduce their negative influence on our body.

Because in our climatic zone we need mostly food of a warming nature, by applying certain principles, we have to try and make it always more Yang. We need to choose first the way of cooking, then the suitable spices and compose them together with the appropriate flavours. Do not be afraid of a cooking process or adding spices! Either way of cooking injects energy into our food and makes it more Yang.

Depending on the needs, we can cook by boiling in water, steaming, pressure cooking, stewing, frying, roasting in an oven, grilling and spit grilling. The most beneficial and energizing is cooking on an open fire (wood, coal, gas).

The time taken to cook is important, too, e.g. a soup cooked for five hours, and with the addition of appropriate ingredients, has an enormous energetic charge with strong medicinal properties and improves the Yang of the body (energy and warmth). We should serve it under special circumstances, when our body is extremely overcooled and weakened. A soup made in a rush and cooked for a short time has a much lower value (even when it contains the right ingredients) than a soup that has been cooked for a long time.

In order to increase the warming and taste properties of, for example, a meat-veg stew, we should initially quick-fry all of the ingredients in some hot oil. We can do the same with grains; for example, we can roast millet, rice or semolina before cooking. Fried or roast potatoes are also much more Yang than boiled potatoes. All vegetables increase their Yang nature during the cooking process, too.

In order to achieve satisfying results in the kitchen, we should not only learn how to put together particular ingredients to get a tasty and healthy dish, but also how to put together different dishes to get a well-balanced meal. This kind of skill is achievable, but it takes time to learn and practise. The whole learning process should begin with a thorough analysis of the rules of a balanced nutrition. We need to reflect upon it and try to understand it properly. Only then can we really get started. At the beginning, we may find it easier to follow the rules rigidly. But once we learn the rules of the Five Flavours and the Five Elements Theory, then we can feel free to use our culinary imagination and cook according to our preferences.

The content of this book may seem at the beginning a bit hard to understand and apply correctly. We should not give up, though. Merely follow the rules of a balanced nutrition and everything will become clearer with time and experience.

In order to really enjoy our cooking adventure and fulfil our culinary fantasies, we need to make sure that we have all of the required basic ingredients in your kitchen. For example:

- Herbs and spices – basil, thyme, oregano, rosemary, garden savory, tarragon, marjoram, sage, nigella, mustard seeds, cumin, ground coriander, sweet and hot paprika, allspice, bay leaves, nutmeg, cinnamon, cloves, cardamom, turmeric, saffron, pepper (black, white, green, cayenne), chilli, ginger, herbal pepper and five-spice powder.

- Herbs for teas – liquorice, thyme, aniseed, lime flowers, marigold flowers, camomile, peppermint, forest fruits.

- Natural coffee, chicory coffee and cocoa.

- Rapeseed and multi-floral honey.

- Fats – olive oil, vegetable oils (rapeseed, soya bean, sunflower), butter, lard.

- Mayonnaise.

- Grains – oats, pearl barley, millet, buckwheat, cornmeal, white and brown rice, semolina, couscous.

- Flours and pasta – plain flour, whole-wheat flour, corn flour, potato starch, and various kinds of pasta.

- Meats – it is advisable to keep a weekly supply of different meats in the fridge, such as lamb, pork, beef, turkey, chicken, veal, meat on bones, pancetta or bacon.

- Vegetables – onion and garlic should be in our kitchen all the time; but in the fridge we can always store a few carrots, parsnips, parsley roots, some cabbage, leeks and celeriac.

- We should also keep some split pea, lentils and beans.

- Dry vegetable powder (stock) – it is not necessary to use it, but if you do decide to do so make sure you use it in moderate quantities.

The recipes I suggest in this book may seem at the beginning quite long and complicated. But appearances can be misleading! This form of presenting the recipes is necessary in order to make them clearer and to avoid mistakes. Each recipe includes the order of adding particular ingredients (flavours) according to the Five Elements Theory. The quantities of spices are mere suggestions and everyone can use as much spice as they like, according to their personal preferences. If we are not used to using many spices in our cooking then it is best to introduce them gradually, slowly increasing their quantities. If we really do not like one of the spices then we should replace it with another, but one of the same flavour.

These recipes are very tasty and popular. They are the basic ones and it is totally up to you how you develop them. All of the recipes from cookery books and magazines can be modified accordingly to the Five Elements Theory, too. You just need to remember that first you need to divide all the ingredients into particular flavours. If one of the flavours should be missing, then you can fill in the gap according to your own taste.

Most of the recipes presented here are of a neutral-warming nature, except for those which are originally sour and thus of neutral-cooling nature. You can use these recipes throughout the whole year and alongside any health condition; you just need to add the appropriate amounts of spices (add more or less, depending on your needs).

We should add the ingredients according to the order of the Five Flavours: bitter – sweet – spicy – salty – sour – bitter – sweet… etc. (see Fig. 11).

When preparing broths or soups based on meat or bone stock, one should follow these rules:

- We can but we do not have to use meat in soups; it is also entirely up to you how much meat you use, but I would suggest using a small portion.

- We must not use chicken in sour soups.

- Calf bones or veal should be put straight into boiling water with thyme.

- Pig's bones or pork should be put either into cold water or boiling water with thyme, cumin and ginger.

- Sheep bones or lamb should be put into boiling water.

- Turkey bones or meat should be put into boiling water with thyme and cumin.

- Chicken bones or meat should be put in cold water or to boiling water with cumin, ginger and salt.

- Goose meat should be put into boiling water with thyme.

# RECIPES

Abbreviations used in recipes:

- S    – sour flavour
- B    – bitter flavour
- SW – sweet flavour
- SP – spicy flavour
- SL – salty flavour

## SOUPS

### Breakfast Soup

B    – to 1½ l of boiling water add:

B    – pinch of turmeric powder

SW – 2 tbsp. millet

SP  – 3 tbsp. oats

SP  – pinch of ginger powder

SL  – salt

Cook it all together for 30 min and then add:

S    – 1 tsp. lemon juice

B    – add more boiling water (if necessary)

B    – 5 walnuts, chopped (optional)

Cook for further 10 min. and then add:

SW – butter and honey, to taste

Cook for 1 minute.

You can cook this soup the night before serving. Instead of millet and oats, you can use cornmeal (SW), wheat flakes (S) and barley flakes (SP), quinoa flakes (B). And you can replace the boiling water (in the second run) with some milk, but always add it when it is time for the sweet-flavoured ingredients.

## Chicken and Beef Broth

(serves 8)

B    – to 4 l of boiling water add:

B    – ⅓ tsp. thyme and/or pinch of turmeric

SW  – ⅓ tsp. cumin

SW  – ½ kg beef or veal on the bone (e.g. beef shank)

Cook it all together for 1½ hours and then add:

SW  – 4–5 medium carrots, cut in half

SW  – 1 large parsnip (or parsley root, if available), cut in half

SP   – 2 large onions or 1 leek and piece of celeriac

SP   – 3 garlic cloves, chopped

SP   – ½ tsp. ginger powder

SP   – pinch of cayenne pepper

SL  – salt, to taste

S    – ½ chicken

S    – pinch of basil

S    – small bunch of fresh parsley, few leaves of celery and bunch of fresh dill, tied together with a string

Cook it all together for 1 hour.

Then take the meat and vegetables out of the soup; pour in some more boiling water (B) and add a pinch of dry marjoram (B), pinch of cumin powder (SW), black and white pepper to taste (SP), and eventually some salt (SL). You can serve it with pasta, egg noodles, potatoes, couscous or cornmeal. The meat you can use in pancake stuffing.

If you want the broth to have strongly warming properties then you should cook it only with beef, veal or lamb.

## Tomato Soup

B    – to 2–3 l of boiling water add:

B    – pinch of thyme and turmeric

SW   – ½ tsp. cumin

SW   – cow's or calf's bones (to taste) or 1 tsp. butter

Cook for 1½ hours and then add:

SW   – 3 medium carrots, chopped

SW   – 1 large parsnip (or parsley root, if available), chopped

SP    – 3 large onions, finely chopped

SP    – 3 garlic cloves, crushed

SP    – ½ tsp. ginger powder

SP    – pinch of cayenne pepper

SL    – salt, to taste

Cook for about 1 hour; then take the bones out of the soup and add:

S    – ½ l tomato juice (homemade)

S    – pinch of basil

B    – boiling water (if necessary)

B    – pinch of marjoram

SW   – egg noodles

If you cook the soup without bones then you should add 1 tsp. of butter (SW), plus some pepper (SP) and salt (SL) to taste. In the summer, you can also add some chopped fresh parsley (S).

## Egg Noodles

SW   – 1 egg

SP    – pinch of ginger powder

SL    – 1 tbsp. water

S    – 1 heaped tbsp. flour

B    –  pinch of turmeric

Mix it all together and then pour thin strings of the mixture on to boiling water.

## Ukrainian Borscht

B    – to 2–3 l of boiling water add:

B    – pinch of dry thyme and turmeric

SW   – beef or veal on the bone (to taste) or 1 tsp. butter

SW   – pinch of cumin

Cook it all together for 1½ hours and then add:

SW   – 1 carrot, finely chopped

SW   – 1 parsnip (or parsley root, if available), finely chopped

SW   – 2–3 medium beetroots, finely chopped

SW   – ½ kg potatoes, finely chopped

SP   – 2 onions, finely chopped

SP   – 3 garlic cloves, crushed

SP   – quarter of small white or Savoy cabbage, finely chopped

SP   – ½ tsp. ginger

SP   – pinch of cayenne pepper

SL   – salt, to taste

SL   – 1 cup of soaked beans (only in spring and summer)

S    – pinch of basil (in summer use fresh basil)

Cook it all together for 1 hour (until all soft)

S    – add ½ cup of water mixed with 2 tbsp. plain wheat flour

S    – lemon juice, to taste

B    – pinch of dry marjoram

take the bones out of the soup

B    – add boiling water

SW  – add 1 tsp. butter (if you are not cooking it with bones)

SP  – pepper and salt (SL), to taste

## Bean Soup

Soak beans the night before cooking (do not use the soaking water in the soup).

B    – to 2–3 l of boiling water add:

B    – pinch of thyme and ⅓ tsp. turmeric

SW  – beef or veal on the bone

SW  – ½ tsp. cumin

Cook it all together for 1½ hours and then add:

SW  – 3 carrots, finely chopped

SW  – 1 parsnip (or parsley root, if available), finely chopped

SW  – 5–6 potatoes, finely chopped

SP  – 3 onions, chopped

SP  – 3 garlic cloves, crushed

SP  – ½ tsp. ginger and ½ tsp. summer savory

SP  – pinch of cayenne pepper

SL  – soaked beans

SL  – 1 tsp. salt

S   – pinch of basil (can be fresh)

S   – bunch of chopped fresh parsley or other greens

B    – marjoram, to taste

Cook it all together until all soft.

Take the meat out of the soup

B    – and add boiling water, then add:

SW  – 1 tsp. butter

SP — white/black pepper and salt (SL), to taste

Instead of potatoes, at the end of cooking (after adding boiling water (B)) you can add some egg noodles (SW) or pasta (SW).

## Pearl Barley Soup

B — to 2–3 l of boiling water add:

B — pinch of thyme and turmeric

SW — ½ tsp. cumin

SP — turkey meat on the bone (wing, drumstick, etc.)

SP — 5–6 tbsp. pearl barley

SP — 1 bay leaf, 4 grains allspice

SP — ½ tsp. ginger

Cook it all together for 1½ hours and then add:

SP — 2 onions or 2 leeks, finely chopped

SP — quarter of Savoy cabbage, finely chopped

SP — in summer add 1 kohlrabi, finely chopped

SL — 2 tsp. salt

S — pinch of basil

S — bunch of chopped fresh parsley or other greens

B — pinch of marjoram

B — add boiling water

SW — 3–4 carrots, finely chopped

SW — 1 large parsnip (or parsley root, if available), chopped

SW — 2–3 potatoes, chopped

Cook it all together for ½ an hour (until all vegetables are soft), then add pepper (SP), salt (SL) and fresh parsley (S), to taste.

## Onion Soup

B    – to 2–3 l of boiling water or vegetable stock add:

B    – pinch of turmeric

SW  – 600–700 g chopped onion, stewed with 1 tbsp. of butter

SP   – ½ tsp. ginger powder

SL   – salt, to taste

Cook it all together for ½ an hour until all soft, then blend the soup and add:

S    – pinch of basil

S    – 1–2 tsp. lemon juice or 1 glass white wine

B    – add boiling water

B    – pinch of marjoram

SW  – pinch of cumin

SP   – pepper and salt (SL), to taste

Serve with croutons or plain.

## Split Pea Soup

SL   – to 2–3 l of cold water add:

S    – piece of chicken

S    – pinch of basil

Bring it to the boil and then add:

B    – pinch of thyme

B    – ⅓ tsp. turmeric

SW  – ½ kg split pea

Cook it all together for 1 hour and then add:

SW  – 2 carrots, finely chopped

SW  – 1 parsnip (or parsley root, if available), chopped

SW  – 2–3 potatoes, chopped

SP   – 2 onions, chopped

SP   – 2 garlic cloves, crushed

SP   – piece of celeriac, chopped or a piece of cabbage, finely chopped

SP   – ½ tsp. ginger

SP   – pinch of cayenne pepper

SL   – salt, to taste

Cook it all together until soft and then add:

S     – bunch of chopped fresh greens or 1 tbsp. lemon juice

B     – pinch of marjoram

B     – add with boiling water

SW  – 1 tsp. butter

Pepper (SP) and salt (SL) to taste.

## Soup à la Napolitana

SL   – to 2 l of pure boiling broth add:

S     – bunch of finely chopped dill

B     – pinch of dry thyme

SW  – pasta, already cooked

SW  – 100 ml single cream

SP   – pepper, to taste

SL   – salt, to taste

Bring it all to the boil.

## Sweet Cabbage Soup

B     – to 2–3 l of boiling water add:

B     – pinch of thyme and turmeric

SW  – cow's bone or other bones

SW  – ½ tsp. cumin

Cook it all together for 1½ hours and then add:

SW  – 2 carrots, sliced

SW  – 1 parsnip (or parsley root, if available), sliced

SW  – 4–5 medium potatoes, diced

SP  – 2 onions, chopped

SP  – 1 garlic clove, crushed

SP  – ¼ medium white cabbage, finely chopped

SP  – 1 bay leaf, 3–4 grains allspice, pinch of cayenne pepper

SL  – salt, to taste

S  – pinch of basil

Cook it all together until soft and then add:

S  – ½ cup of water mixed with 2 tbsp. of plain wheat flour

S  – lemon juice, to taste (the flavour should be mild though)

If necessary add some marjoram (B), cumin (SW), pepper (SP) and salt (SL).

## Small Round Noodles Soup

B  – to 2 l of boiling water add:

B  – pinch of thyme and turmeric

SW  – 600 g potatoes, chopped (choose rather softer kind of potatoes)

SW  – pinch of cumin

SP  – 3 onions, finely chopped

SP  – ½ tsp. ginger

SP  – pinch of cayenne pepper

SL  – salt, to taste

Cook it all together until soft and then add:

S  – pinch of basil

S    – small round noodles

Cook for another ½ an hour and then add:

B    – pinch of marjoram

SW  – 1 tbsp. butter

SP   – pepper and salt (SL), to taste

Small round noodles: to 4–5 tbsp. of plain wheat flour keep adding cold water and knead it thoroughly until you obtain a hard dough; then pick small noodles and roll them in flour.

## Beetroot Leaf Soup

B    – to 2–3 l of boiling water add:

B    – pinch of thyme and turmeric

SW  – cow's bone

Cook it all together for 1 hour and then add:

SW  – 3 carrots, chopped

SW  – 1 parsnip (or parsley root, if available), chopped

SP   – 2 onions, chopped

SP   – 3 garlic cloves, chopped

SP   – ½ tsp. ginger

SP   – pinch of cayenne pepper

SL   – salt, to taste

S    – bunch of chopped fresh parsley and dill

S    – ½ kg chopped young beetroots with leaves

Cook it all together for 40 min then add:

S    – ½ cup of water mixed with 2 tbsp. of plain wheat flour

S    – 1–2 tsp. lemon juice, to taste

B    – add boiling water; then add:

B    – pinch of marjoram (preferably fresh)

SW   – 1 tbsp. butter (if the soup is not based on bones)

You can serve the soup together with fried potatoes with cumin.

## Button Mushroom Soup

B    – to 2–3 l of boiling water add:

B    – pinch of thyme and turmeric

SW   – beef or veal on the bone

Cook it all together for 1 hour and then add:

SW   – 3 whole carrots

SW   – 1 whole parsnip (or parsley root, if available)

Cook it all until soft; then take the meat and vegetables out of the soup (you can use them, for example, in salads) and add:

SW   – 600 g button mushrooms, chopped

SP   – 4 onions, finely chopped

SP   – ½ tsp. ginger

SP   – pinch of cayenne pepper

SL   – salt, to taste

Cook for another 45 min.; then blend the soup and add:

S    – pinch of basil

S    – ½ tsp. lemon juice

S    – bunch of chopped fresh parsley

B    – add boiling water

B    – pinch of marjoram

You can also add 100 ml of single cream (SW) and pepper (SP) and salt (SL) to taste. Serve with pasta or egg noodles.

## Green Pea or Corn Soup

B     – to 2–3 l of boiling water add:

B     – pinch of thyme and turmeric

SW  – cow's or calf's bone

Cook it all together for 1½ hours and then add:

SW  – 3 carrots, chopped

SW  – 4 potatoes, chopped

SW  – 1 parsnip (or parsley root, if available), chopped

SP   – a small piece of celeriac, chopped

SP   – 2 onions, chopped

SP   – 2 garlic cloves, chopped

SP   – ½ tsp. ginger

SP   – pinch of cayenne pepper

SL   – salt, to taste

Cook it all together for 30 min. and then add:

S    – bunch of chopped fresh parsley or other greens

B    – add boiling water

B    – pinch of marjoram

SW  – can of green peas or corn with brine

SW  – ½ cup of cold water mixed with 2 tbsp. of corn flour

SW  – 1 tbsp. butter (if the soup is not based on bones)

SW  – pinch of cumin

SP   – pepper and salt (SL), to taste

## Leek Soup

B    – to 2–3 l of boiling water add:

B    – pinch of thyme and turmeric

SW  – pinch of cumin

SW  – 1 kg potatoes, chopped

SP  – 600 g leeks, chopped (you can stew them with some butter first; this way the soup gains more flavour)

SP  – ½ tsp. ginger powder

SP  – pinch of cayenne pepper

SL  – salt, to taste

Cook it all together until soft; then blend the soup and add:

S  – pinch of basil or chopped fresh parsley or 1 tsp. lemon juice

B  – add some boiling water and add:

SW  – 1 tbsp. butter (if not added earlier)

SP  – pepper and salt (SL) to taste

Serve with croutons or plain.

## Gold Vegetable Soup

B  – to 2–3 l of boiling water add:

B  – pinch of thyme and turmeric

SW  – 7 medium carrots, chopped

SW  – 4 large potatoes, chopped

SW  – 1 parsnip (or parsley root, if available), chopped

SP  – 3 onions, chopped

SP  – ½ tsp. ginger

SP  – pinch of cayenne pepper

SL  – salt, to taste

Cook it all together until soft; then blend the soup and add:

S  – bunch of chopped fresh parsley or other greens

S  – 1 tsp. lemon juice

B  – add boiling water

Serve with croutons or plain.

## Celeriac Soup

B     – to 2–3 l of boiling water add:

B     – pinch of thyme and turmeric

SW    – 2 medium carrots, chopped

SW    – ½ kg potatoes, chopped

SP     – 1 large celeriac, chopped

SP     – 1 onion, chopped

SP     – 2 garlic cloves, chopped

SP     – ½ tsp. ginger

SP     – pinch of cayenne pepper

SL     – salt, to taste

Cook it all together for 1 hour until soft; then blend the soup and add:

S     – pinch of basil

S     – ½ tsp. lemon juice or 2 tbsp. chopped fresh parsley

B     – add boiling water (if necessary)

B     – pinch of marjoram

SW    – 1 tbsp. butter

SW    – pinch of cumin

SP     – pepper and salt (SL), to taste

Serve with croutons or plain.

## Spring Soup

B     – to 2–3 l of boiling water add:

B     – pinch of thyme and turmeric

SW    – cow's or calf's bones

Cook it all together for 1 hour and then add:

SW  – 600 g potatoes, chopped

SP  – large bunch of spring onions, chopped

SP  – 2 garlic cloves, chopped

SP  – ½ tsp. ginger

SP  – pinch of pepper

SL  – salt, to taste

S  – chopped bunch of each of these greens: young kohlrabi leaves, celery leaves, parsley, dill

Cook it all together for 30 min. until all soft.

B  – if necessary, add boiling water

B  – pinch of marjoram or turmeric

SW  – 1 tbsp. butter (when there are no bones)

SW  – pinch of cumin

SP  – pepper and salt (SL), to taste

## Vegetable Soup

B  – to 2–3 l of boiling water add:

B  – pinch of thyme

SW  – cow's or calf's bone

Cook it all together for 1 hour and then add:

SW  – 3 carrots, chopped

SW  – ½ kg new potatoes, chopped

SW  – 150 g young peas

SP  – ½ young cabbage, chopped and/or 2 kohlrabi, chopped

SP  – bunch of spring onions, chopped

SP  – ½ tsp. ginger

SP  – pepper

SL  – salt, to taste

S    – chopped greens (kohlrabi leaves, celery leaves, parsley)

Cook it all together for 30 min.

B    – add boiling water, if necessary, and then add:

B    – pinch of marjoram

You can make this soup without potatoes and put some egg noodles or pasta in it instead (at the end of cooking). You can also thicken the soup by adding (together with the greens) some semolina.

## Sorrel Soup

Cook 300–400 g of sorrel in a small amount of water and then blend it.

B    – to 2–3 l of boiling water add:

B    – pinch of thyme and ⅓ tsp. turmeric

SW  – cow's or calf's bone

Cook it all together for 1 hour and then add:

SW  – 3–4 carrots, cut in half

SW  – 1 parsnip (or parsley root, if available), cut in half

SP  – 2 whole onions

SP  – piece of celeriac

SP  – ½ tsp. ginger

SP  – pepper

SL  – salt, to taste

Cook it all until soft; then take the meat and vegetables out of the soup (use them in a salad).

S    – keep gradually adding blended sorrel, but make sure that the soup is not too sour

B    – add boiling water (if necessary)

SW  – 100 ml sweet single cream or ½ tbsp. butter (to taste)

SP  – pepper and salt (SL), to taste

Serve with boiled egg or potatoes.

## Sour Rye Soup

B    – to 2–3 l of boiling water add:

B    – pinch of thyme

B    – 200 g of pancetta (optional)

SW   – beef on the bone

*Cook for 1 hour and then add:*

SW   – 4 whole carrots

SW   – 1 whole parsnip (or parsley root, if available)

SP    – 2 whole onions

SP    – 3 garlic cloves, pressed

SP    – ½ tsp. ginger

SP    – pinch of pepper

SL    – salt, to taste

Cook it all together for 1 hour; then take the meat and vegetables out of the soup and add:

S    – sourdough liquid (to taste, but the soup should not be too sour)

B    – add boiling water, if necessary

B    – 1 tsp. marjoram

SW   – ½ tsp. cumin

SW   – 100 ml sweet single cream (to taste)

SP    – pepper and salt (SL)

Serve with potatoes, boiled egg, chopped sausage (cooked separately) or chopped pancetta from the soup. The vegetables you can use in salads.

## Autumn Soup

B  – to 2–3 l boiling water add:

B  – pinch of thyme and ⅓ tsp. turmeric

SW  – cow's or calf's bone

Cook it all together for 1 hour and then add:

SW  – 3 carrots, chopped

SW  – 1 parsnip (or parsley root, if available), chopped

SW  – ½ kg potatoes, chopped

SP  – ½ Savoy cabbage, chopped

SP  – 1 onion, chopped

SP  – 2 garlic cloves, chopped

SP  – ½ tsp. ginger

SP  – pinch of pepper

SL  – 150g fresh beans, peeled

SL  – salt, to taste

S  – 1 large tomato, peeled and chopped

S  – bunch of chopped fresh parsley

Cook it all together until all soft.

S  – add ½ cup of cold water mixed with 2 tbsp. plain wheat flour

B  – add boiling water

B  – pinch of marjoram (preferably fresh) and turmeric

SW  – 1 tbsp. butter (if there are no bones in the soup

SW  – sweet cream, to taste

SP  – pepper and salt (SL)

## Clear Borscht

Beetroot stock:

B  – to 2 l of boiling water add:

B — pinch of thyme and ⅓ tsp. turmeric

SW — 1 kg beetroots, grated

SW — 1 tsp. cumin

SP — ⅓ tsp. ginger

SL — 1 tsp. salt

Cook it all together for 10 min., then leave to rest for 1–2 hours.


**For meat and vegetable stock:**

B — to 2 l of boiling water add:

B — pinch of turmeric

SW — 600 g beef on the bone

SW — ½ tsp. cumin

Cook it all together for 1 hour and then add:

SW — 2 carrots, cut in half

SW — 1 parsnip (or parsley root, if available), cut in half

SP — a small piece of celeriac

SP — 2–3 whole onions and 4 whole garlic cloves

SP — ½ tsp. ginger

SP — pinch of cayenne pepper, 1 bay leaf, 5 grains allspice

Cook it all together for 1 hour.

Strain beetroot stock and meat and vegetable stock to a large casserole then add:

SP — pepper, to taste

SL — salt, to taste

SL — 150 g dried porcini mushrooms stock, to taste

S — 1 tbsp. lemon juice

B — ½ glass (100 ml) dry red wine

SW — some honey, if necessary (to taste)

SP   – some more pepper and salt (SL), to taste

Serve with pastries, meat dumplings or on its own.

## Summer Split Pea Soup

SL   – to 2–3 l of cold water add:

SL   – cow's or chicken bones

S   – pinch of basil

B   – pinch of thyme and ⅓ tsp. turmeric

SW   – pinch of cumin

Cook it all together for 1 hour and then add:

SW   – 400 g split pea

Cook it for 1 hour; then take the bones out and blend the soup; then add:

SW   – 2 carrots, sliced

SP   – 2 kohlrabi, chopped

SP   – ¼ young cabbage, chopped

SP   – bunch of spring onions, chopped

SP   – ½ tsp. ginger

SP   – pinch of cayenne pepper

SL   – salt, to taste

S   – 2 handful chopped greens (parsley, celery leaves, dill, kohlrabi leaves)

Cook it all together for 30 min. until soft.

B   – add boiling water

SW   – add egg noodles

SW   – 1 tbsp. butter

SP   – pepper and salt (SL), to taste

# VEGETARIAN RECIPIES

## Boiled Potatoes

B   – to ½ l of boiling water add:

B   – pinch of turmeric

SW  – ½ tsp. cumin

SW  – ½ tsp. butter (if you decide to keep the water)

SW  – 1 kg peeled potatoes

SP  – 1 onion, chopped

SP  – 2 garlic cloves

SL  – 1 tsp. salt

Boil the potatoes until soft (there should not be much water left) together with all the ingredients.

New potatoes can be boiled in their skins. You can peel them after cooking and fry with butter or olive oil, adding the following spices: cumin, pepper, salt, greens, turmeric and fresh marjoram.

## Pancakes

(quantity for 6 pancakes)

S   – to 300 ml of plain wheat flour add:

B   – pinch of turmeric

SW  – 1 egg

SP  – ¼ tsp. ginger

SP  – pinch of freshly grated nutmeg

SL  – pinch of salt

SL  – 320 ml water

Mix all the ingredients with half of the water (use a wooden spoon for mixing). Once the consistency of the batter is smooth, add the rest of the water.

If you prefer sweet pancakes then together with the egg add a teaspoon of liquid honey (but skip the nutmeg in this case).

Bake each pancake on both sides in a hot pan with a small amount of oil.

## Sweet Cabbage Stuffing

(for a double portion of pancakes)

Cut one small cabbage (about 1 kg) in quarters, throw into boiling water and cook until soft. Strain the cabbage (but do not squeeze the water out completely), let it cool down, then mince it (but still do not get rid of the water absorbed by the cabbage!). Fry 2 chopped onions (SW) with 2 tbsp. of oil or 1 tbsp. of butter. Add the minced cabbage (SP) and keep frying on a low heat constantly stirring. At the same time keep adding the following spices: ½ a tsp. ginger (SP), black and cayenne pepper (SP), salt to taste (SL), pinch of basil (S), ½ tsp. lemon juice (S), pinch of thyme and turmeric (B), 1 tsp. cumin (SW). Fry it all together for 30 min. until the water is gone and the cabbage is soft enough. The stuffing should have a rather strong flavour.

## Sweet White Cheese Stuffing

To 300 g of white cheese (S) add pinch of turmeric (B), sweet cream and 1 egg yolk (SW), honey to taste (SW), ¼ tsp. ginger (SP), pinch of salt (SL) and mix it all together thoroughly.

You can also serve the pancakes with homemade jams and marmalades, chocolate or sweet sauces.

## Fried Bananas

Cut 2 ripe bananas in quarters. Then cover them in flour, beaten egg and flour again and fry in a semi-hot pan with some oil and butter. Whilst in the pan, keep sprinkling the bananas with some cinnamon and ginger. If you like, you can pour some honey on top as well.

## White Cheese Gnocchi

S    – to ½ kg of white cheese keep adding and stirring in:

S    – 3–4 tbsp. wheat flour

B    – ⅓ tsp. turmeric

SW  – 3 egg yolks

SP  – ½ tsp. ginger

SL  – pinch of salt

Mix it all together thoroughly with a spoon and then add:

S    – pinch of wheat flour

B    – pinch of turmeric

SW  – 3 egg whites, whisked

Mix it all again. Then form small gnocchi and throw them in to salty boiling water and cook for 2–3 min.

Serve them with melted butter, runny honey and cinnamon.

## Omelette with Button Mushrooms

SW  – fry for 15 min. 200 g of sliced button mushrooms with 1 tbsp. of oil or butter; keep also adding the following ingredients:

SW  – pinch of cumin

SP  – pepper (to taste)

SP  – 1 small garlic clove, pressed

SL  – salt (to taste)

S    – 1 tsp. fresh chopped parsley

S    – pinch of thyme

Preparation of the omelette:

SW  – beat 2 eggs with a fork and add:

SP  – white pepper (to taste)

SL    – 2 tbsp. water

SL    – salt (to taste)

Mix it all together with a fork and pour it in to a hot pan; fry it for a moment lifting the edges of the omelette and making sure that all the liquid goes to the bottom of the pan.

Place the omelette on a plate, fill it with the mushroom stuffing and fold in half. Serve it with fried ham or sausages, green peas or corn and some homemade ketchup.

## Potato Pancakes

SW   – to 1 kg of finely grated potatoes add:

SW   – 1 flat tbsp. corn flour

SW   – 2–3 eggs

SP    – 1 onion, finely grated

SP    – 1 big garlic clove, finely grated

SP    – black pepper

SL    – salt (to taste)

S     – 1 tbsp. plain wheat flour

B     – pinch of turmeric

Mix it all together thoroughly and bake small pancakes in a hot pan with some oil.

Serve it with sour milk, sour cream or probiotic yogurt.

## Pearl Barley Croquettes

SW   – to 450 g of cooked pearl barley add:

SW   – 250 g cooked minced meat (or/and ham, sausages, bacon)

SW   – cooked minced vegetables (carrot, parsnip, or parsley root, if available), a piece of celeriac, onion, leek)

SW  – 1 egg

SP  – ½ tsp. ginger, black pepper, pinch of coriander

Mix it all together and then add:

SL  – salt

S  – pinch of basil

B  – pinch of marjoram

Form small croquettes, coat first in egg and then in breadcrumbs and fry in a medium hot pan with some oil. You can serve them with ketchup.


## MEAT AND MEAT-VEG RECIPIES

### Risotto

Finely chop ½ kg of cooked or roasted meat leftovers with some added bacon or ham. Fry it in a pan with 1 tbsp. of oil.

Chop 4 large onions and 3 garlic cloves and fry them with some oil until golden.

SW  – wash and then dry on a paper towel 225 g of rice; heat in a casserole 3 tbsp. of oil, add the rice and fry it for 15 min. constantly stirring, then take off the hob

SW  – mix the fried meat with the onion and garlic and a can of peas together with the brine and then add:

SP  – the fried rice

SP  – 1 tsp. ginger

SP  – pinch of cayenne and black pepper (to taste)

SP  – ½ tsp. coriander

SL  – salt (to taste)

Mix it all together and then add:

S  – pinch of basil and bunch of chopped fresh parsley

B   – ¼ tsp. turmeric

B   – ½ l of boiling water

SW  – 1 tbsp. butter

Mix it thoroughly, bring it to the boil and place in the oven for about 1 hour (150 °C).

## Meat and Vegetable Stuffing ( for pancakes)

Mince all cooked meat and vegetables that you have previously used in a soup or a broth and fry it in a hot pan (with 1 tbsp. of oil). Add some cumin, different kinds of pepper, ½ tsp. ginger, salt to taste, pinch of basil and marjoram. Fry it all together for about 10 min.

## Meat Marinade

Mix all together:

SW  – 1 tsp. potato starch

SP  – ½ tsp. of ginger

SL  – 1 tsp. soya sauce or ½ tsp. salt

SL  – 3–4 tbsp. of cold water

You can use this marinade for cutlets, chops, steaks, schnitzels and all kinds of meat (even in goulash or stew). This amount of marinade is sufficient for ½ kg of meat. Make sure that it is well absorbed by the meat.

Remember that all sliced and plain meat (with no marinade or breadcrumbs) should be seasoned whilst being fried in a pan, not earlier!

## Pork Breaded Cutlets

Pound with a mallet some boneless pork tenderloin slices (SL). Place the meat in a previously prepared marinade (see recipe) and leave to rest for 20 min.

Then season it lightly with pepper (SP), salt (SL), a few drops of lemon juice (S) and pinch of turmeric (B).

Beat an egg and mix it with a pinch of cayenne pepper. Dip the meat in the egg and then cover it in breadcrumbs or flour. Fry it with some oil in a medium hot pan for about 10 min. on each side.3

## Ribs with Cabbage

SL – rub with a marinade 1 kg of small pork ribs (marinade: 1 tsp. potato starch, 1 tsp. ginger, 1 tbsp. soya sauce or 1 tsp. salt, 2–3 tbsp. water mixed all together), then leave them to rest for 30 min.

In a large casserole bring to the boil 600 ml of water and add:

B     – pinch of thyme

B     – ½ tsp. turmeric

SW  – 1 tsp. cumin

SW  – 3 large onions, chopped and gently fired with 1 tbsp. of oil

SP   – ½ a bay leaf, 4 grains allspice, ¼ tsp. coriander, pinch of cayenne pepper

Fry the ribs briefly in a frying pan with a small amount of oil; then put them into the water with spices and add:

SL   – 1 tsp. salt and stir properly

Stew the ribs under cover for about 1½ hours and then add:

S     – pinch of basil

S     – 1 tbsp. lemon juice

B     – add boiling water, so the ribs are completely covered with the sauce and add:

SW  – ½ tsp. cumin

SP   – 1 small young cabbage (chopped) or ½ old and previously cooked cabbage (chopped); stir it all together and cook until soft (about 30 min.)

SP   – pepper and salt (SL) to taste

Serve with the boiled potatoes (see recipe) or bread.

## Spicy Ribs

SL    – marinade (see recipe for the marinade) 1 kg of small pork ribs and leave them to soak for 30 min.

SW   – slice 3 medium carrots, fry them for 2 min. in 100 ml of hot oil, then strain them and place in a large casserole

SW   – using the same oil, fry 3 large onions (chopped), strain and add them to the carrots (stewed onion acquires the sweet flavour)

SW   – add 1 tsp. of cumin

SP    – using the same oil, fry ¼ of a celeriac (chopped), and add to the other vegetables; then add:

SP    – 1 tsp. coriander, ⅓ tsp. cayenne pepper, some black pepper

SL    – using the same oil, fry briefly the ribs and then place together with the vegetables

SL    – add 400 ml of cold water and some salt to taste (1–2 tsp.); cover the casserole and place it in the oven; stew the ribs until soft and then add:

S     – pinch of basil and 1 tsp. lemon juice, stir it and add:

B     – pinch of turmeric or thyme and marjoram

SW   – pinch of cumin

SP    – taste it now (the ribs should be rather hot and spicy) and if necessary add some ginger, cayenne pepper or chilli

SL    – add some salt (to taste) and stew for another 10 min.

Altogether, the ribs should be stewed for about 2 hours in the oven preheated to 140 °C.

Serve with noodles and cooked cauliflower or boiled potatoes (see recipe) and gherkins.

## Stewed Sweet Ribs

SL – prepare a marinade: 1 heaped tsp. potato starch, 1 tsp. ginger, 3–4 tsp. vodka, 1 tbsp. soya sauce; mix 1 kg of small pork ribs with the marinade and leave them to rest for 1 hour

Heat a frying pan with 3 tbsp. of oil, fry the ribs briefly on each side and then place them in a casserole; then add:

SL   – 1 tsp. salt (to taste)

SL   – ½ l cold water, stir it and add:

S    – 1 tbsp. lemon juice and pinch of basil

B    – pinch of turmeric and thyme

SW  – ½ tsp. cumin and 1 heaped tbsp. honey

SP   – 2 tsp. five-spice powder, ¼ tsp. cayenne and black pepper, stir it all and stew under cover in the oven for about 2 hours (140 °C).

The ribs should be rather hot and spicy. Serve with white bread, olives and plum sauce or with potatoes and French beans.

## Roast Loin of Pork

SL   – pound with a mallet 1½ kg of boneless pork loin, then rub it with the following spices:

SL   – 1½ tsp. salt

B    – ½ tsp. basil and 1 tsp. lemon juice

B    – ½ tsp. marjoram and pinch of turmeric

SW  – 1 tbsp. olive oil

SP   – ½ tsp. ginger

SP   – pinch of black and cayenne pepper

Leave it to rest for 1 hour. Preheat the oven to the maximum temperature. Then tie the pork loin with a string, place it in a large casserole and roast without cover for about 20 min. Then do the following:

SW  – sprinkle the meat with 1 tsp. cumin

SP   – add 2 onions, chopped

Cover the casserole, reduce the heat to 120 °C and roast the meat for 1½ hours. Then take the meat out, cut into slices and leave it in a warm place (e.g. oven). With the gravy you can make some sauce:

SL — pour in to the casserole ½ l of cold water, bring it to the boil, add some salt to taste; then add:

S — ½ tsp. lemon juice

B — pinch of thyme and turmeric

SW — 1 tbsp. butter

SW — ⅓ cup of water mixed with 1–2 tsp. potato starch

Add some pepper (SP) and salt (SL) to taste.

Serve the meat with potatoes, all kinds of grains, boiled or stewed vegetables and fresh salads.


## Roast Pork

SL — pound with a mallet 1½ kg of pork then rub it with:

SL — some salt (to taste)

S — ⅓ tsp. basil and 1 tsp. lemon juice

B — 2 tsp. marjoram, pinch of turmeric and pinch of rosemary

SW — 1 tbsp. olive oil

SP — pinch of black pepper and ½ tsp. ginger

Leave it to rest for ½ an hour. Preheat the oven to the maximum temperature. Roast the meat for about ½ an hour and then add:

SW — 1 tsp. cumin

SP — 2 onions, chopped

Reduce the heat to 140 °C, cover the meat and roast until soft.

If you would like some sauce to go with the meat then prepare it as in the recipe for roast loin of pork. Also, if you like you can always roast the pork with some vegetables.

Serve it with potatoes or grains and all kinds of vegetables prepared according to the recipes from this book.

## Meat Balls

SW  – to 1 kg of minced pork and beef add:

SW  – 1 tsp. potato starch and 2 eggs

SP  – 1 minced onion, ½ tsp. ginger, pinch of cayenne pepper, pinch of coriander, black pepper (to taste)

Mix it all together thoroughly and then add:

SL  – salt (to taste)

S  – 2 bread rolls (soaked in water, then strained and minced)

S  – you can also add a tablespoon of chopped fresh parsley and pinch of basil

B  – ½ tsp. marjoram and pinch of turmeric

Mix it all together once again; then roll small meat balls.

B  – bring to the boil 1½ l of water and then add to it:

B  – pinch of turmeric and thyme

SW  – ½ tsp. cumin

Throw the meat balls in to the water.

SP  – add ⅓ tsp. ginger, ½ a bay leaf, 4 grains allspice and some black pepper (to taste)

SL  – add some salt (to taste)

Cook it all for 20 min. Then add:

S  – pinch of basil and bunch of parsley and dill

S  – ½ cup of cold water mixed with 1 tbsp. plain wheat flour

B  – pinch of marjoram

Cook it for further 10 min. and then add:

SW  – 1 tsp. butter (if the meat is very lean) and some pepper (SP) and salt (SL) to taste.

Serve it with noodles and some boiled vegetables (cauliflower, broccoli, Brussels sprouts, green beans) or potatoes and fresh salads.

## Mince Burger

Prepare the minced meat as for the meat balls. Then form small flattened cutlets, coat them with breadcrumbs and fry in a hot pan with some oil for 10 min on each side.

Serve with potatoes and all kinds of vegetables suggested in this book. Mince burgers are also tasty cold and go nicely in sandwiches.

## Stewed Pork with Vegetables

SL  – cut 300–400 g of lean pork into thin strips (1 cm) and mix it with the meat marinade (see recipe). Leave it to rest for 30 min.

Chop 1 carrot into half rings; chop one leek (the white part) and quarter of a small cabbage.

Fry the vegetables one by one in a frying pan with some oil, then place in a casserole:

SW  – carrot

SP  – leek

SP  – cabbage

SL  – meat

SL  – add 200 ml of cold water, some salt (to taste), and stir it all together; then add:

S  – 1 tomato, peeled and chopped

B  – pinch of thyme and pinch of turmeric

SW  – ⅓ tsp. cumin

SP  – ginger and various peppers (to taste)

SL  – some salt (to taste)

S  – pinch of basil

B  – add some boiling water if necessary

SW – ½ cup of cold water mixed with 1 tbsp. potato starch (make sure that you do not put too much potato starch and that the sauce is not too thick)

In the summer, when the vegetables are young, make sure you add them only 10 min. before the end of cooking.

## Loin of Pork with Bacon and Button Mushrooms

Cut 300 g of pork loin into thin strips (1 cm) and mix with the meat marinade (see recipe). Leave it to rest for 30 min.

SW – in a frying pan (with 5 tbsp. of oil) fry 2 chopped onions and 4 garlic cloves, then drain and place in a casserole

SP – add ¼ tsp. ginger, pinch of cayenne pepper and pinch of black pepper

SL – fry the meat with the rest of oil, then place it in the casserole, stir it and add some salt (to taste); also add:

S – pinch of basil

B – 100 ml boiling water, pinch of thyme and turmeric, stir it and stew under cover for 15 min.

SW – add 400 g of button mushrooms, sliced

SP – some pepper (to taste)

SL – 200 g of bacon, cut into thin strips (½cm)

Stew it all together for 15–20 min. Then add:

SL – some salt (to taste)

S – about 200 ml tomato juice (make sure that the whole dish is not too sour)

B – pinch of thyme

SW – ½ tsp. cumin

SW – ½ cup of cold water mixed with 1 tbsp. potato starch

SP – pepper and salt (SL) to taste

Serve it with noodles, rice, potatoes or white bread.

## Roast Beef

SW  – pound with a mallet 1½ kg of young beef and rub it with:

SW  – 1 tbsp. olive oil

SP  – ⅓ tsp. ginger, black pepper, hot paprika

SL  – 1½ tsp. salt, 1 tsp. soya sauce

S  – 1 tsp. lemon juice and pinch of basil

B  – 1 tsp. thyme

Leave it to rest for 1–2 hours. Preheat the oven to the maximum temperature. Place the meat in a large casserole and put it (uncovered) into the oven for 20 min. Then add:

SP  – 1 bay leaf and 5 grains allspice

SL  – 50 ml of cold water

Cover the casserole, reduce the heat to 130 °C and cook the meat for 2 hours, checking halfway through if it needs more water. When soft, remove the meat from the casserole and cut into slices. Leave it to rest in a warm place (the oven). Then to the gravy add:

SL  – ½ l of cold water, bring it to the boil, add some salt (to taste)

S  – pinch of basil and 1–2 tsp. lemon juice

B  – pinch of thyme and pinch of turmeric

SW  – 1 tsp. honey, 1 tsp. butter

SW  – ½ cup of cold water mixed with 1 tbsp. potato starch

SP  – some pepper (to taste)

Serve with potatoes, beetroot salad and Brussels sprouts or gnocchi, cauliflower and broccoli.

## Beef with Cabbage

B  – to 1 l of boiling water add:

B  – pinch of thyme

SW  – ½ kg of rump steak and ½ tsp. cumin

Cook it under cover on a low heat until soft (around 2 hours). Then remove the meat and cut it into chunks. To the broth add:

SP  – 1 young cabbage, chopped (if the cabbage is old then boil it for a while first)

SP  – 2 chopped onions, ½ tsp. ginger, black and cayenne pepper (to taste), 1 bay leaf, 4 grains allspice

SL  – 2 tsp. salt

S  – 2 ripe tomatoes, peeled and chopped and 100 ml tomato juice

B  – pinch of thyme

Stew the cabbage until soft. Then add:

SW  – ½ tsp. cumin and the cooked meat; you can also thicken it with some potato starch

SP  – some pepper (to taste)

Serve with boiled potatoes or some bread.

## Beef Roll

SW  – slice 1 kg of beef against the grain; pound each slice with a mallet and marinade for ½ an hour (see the recipe for the marinade)

Cut as many slices of smoked pancetta as there are beef slices.

SP  – sprinkle the meat slices with black pepper

SP  – spread some mustard on each slice and then place a thick strip of onion on each one of them

SL  – salt them gently and place a slice of pancetta on top of each slice of meat; then sprinkle them with some basil (S)

Roll the meat slices up into roulades and clamp with toothpicks. Fry them briefly in a pan with some oil; then place in a casserole containing:

B  – 1 l of boiling water with pinch of turmeric and thyme, to which you add:

SW  – 2 large onions, chopped and fried gently with 2 tbsp. of oil

SP — ½ a bay leaf, 4 grains allspice, black pepper and chilli (to taste), pinch of coriander

SL — salt (to taste)

SL — stew it all together for 1½–2 hours, adding some cold water if necessary

S — then thicken the sauce with 1 tbsp. plain wheat flour mixed with cold water and cook for another 10 min. (if you want to add some flavours then start with pinch of basil followed by a grated gherkin (S), pinch of marjoram (B), cumin (SW), pepper (SP) and salt (SL), all the spices to taste)

Serve with yeast steamed dumplings and beetroot salad, gnocchi or potatoes and any boiled vegetables.

### Beef Stew with Vegetables

SW — cut 300–400 g of young beef into strips and mix it with the marinade (see recipe); then leave it to rest for ½ an hour

B — bring to the boil ½ l of water with pinch of thyme and turmeric

SW — in a frying pan with 2–3 tbsp. of oil briefly fry the meat; then place it in a casserole and stew for 1 hour

SW — add ½ kg of button mushrooms (white and healthy), cut into thick slices

SW — in a frying pan with 1 tbsp. of oil briefly fry 2 large onions (cut into half rings) and add them to the meat

SP — fry 250 g chopped sweet or Savoy cabbage and also add it to the meat; then add:

SP — pinch of cayenne pepper and ¼ tsp. black pepper

SL — 1 tsp. salt

S — bunch of chopped mixed greens and 1–2 tsp. lemon juice

Stew until the meat is soft.

B — add some boiling water if necessary and pinch of marjoram

SW — thicken it with 1 tbsp. potato starch mixed with some cold water

SP — add some black pepper and salt (SL) to taste

Serve with rice or noodles and additionally with cauliflower, broccoli or green beans.

## Béchamel Sauce (for cooked chicken meat used previously in a broth)

SW – preheat some oil or butter in a frying pan; add 2–3 tbsp. of plain wheat flour, fry it for a moment until the roux gets a slightly golden colour then leave it to cool

SW – mix 200 ml of cream with 200 ml of cold water, add to the cold roux, mix it thoroughly and warm it up on the hob

SP – add pinch of ginger, white and black pepper; once the mixture starts thickening add to it:

SL – some cold water until the consistency is right, some salt; whilst stirring keep adding:

S – about 2 tsp. lemon juice

B – pinch of turmeric and thyme

SW – 2 egg yolks, beaten and mixed with 4 tbsp. of water; take it off the hob

SW – you can add some honey if you like

Serve it with chicken or turkey meat, cooked previously in a broth, and potatoes or rice, stewed vegetables (e.g. carrots or peas).

## Green Béchamel Sauce

To the standard béchamel sauce, instead of lemon juice, add bunch of various greens (dill, parsley, celeriac leaves, leek leaves and garlic leaves) and cook it all together for 5 min.

It goes nicely with pasta and meats, used previously in broths, or roast meats. Serve it with green beans, cauliflower, broccoli, Brussels sprouts or boiled cabbage.

## Chicken Breast (with sage and vodka)

Pound with a mallet 6 fillets of chicken breast and marinade it (1 tsp. potato starch, ½ tsp. ginger, 4 tbsp. vodka, 1 tsp. salt). Leave it to rest for 30 min.

S — preheat a frying pan with 2 tbsp. of oil and fry the fillets for 2 min. on each side; then reduce the heat

B — sprinkle the fillets with 2 tsp. of sage

SW — add 1 tsp. of butter

SP — black and cayenne pepper, pour 2 tbsp. of vodka all over it

SL — salt (to taste)

Cover the pan and stew the fillets for another 15 min.

Serve with boiled potatoes and any boiled vegetables.

## Chicken Breast with Pineapple

(serves 6)

Dice into small pieces (1½ cm × 1½ cm) ½ kg of chicken meat and marinade it in: 1 tsp. potato starch, ½ tsp. ginger, 1 tsp. salt and 50 ml cold water; mix it all together and leave to rest for 30 min.

S — preheat 100 ml of oil; divide the meat into two portions and then fry it, portion by portion, in the hot oil; drain the meat, place it in a casserole and add:

B — pinch of turmeric

SW — 2 cans of pineapple, cut into pieces, together with the juice

SP — cut ½ kg of leeks (only white parts) into thin slices and fry it in the same oil; then drain and add it to the meat; mix it all together and stew on a low heat for about 10 min.

SP — add some black, white and cayenne pepper to taste (it should be very hot)

SL — add some salt to taste

S — some lemon juice (the dish should have a sour-sweet flavour)

B — add pinch of thyme, some boiling water (until the sauce covers the meat)

SW  – add some honey and thicken the sauce with some potato starch mixed with cold water

SP   – add some pepper and salt (SL)

Serve it with white bread or rice.

## Chicken in Breadcrumbs

S    – remove the bones from the chicken (use the meat you cooked previously in a broth) and with a mallet form it into small cutlets; sprinkle them with the following spices:

B    – turmeric

SW  – cumin

SP   – black and cayenne pepper

SL   – salt

Dip the cutlets in a beaten egg and then cover them with breadcrumbs or plain wheat flour. Preheat a frying pan with some oil. Fry the cutlets on both sides on a medium heat.

Serve them warm or cold. Either way the cutlets are very tasty and great for picnics or during travel.

## Traditional Roast Chicken

S    – 6–8 pieces of chicken (small drumsticks or other parts) rub with:

B    – turmeric, 1 tsp. marjoram

SW  – 1 tbsp. olive oil, 1 tsp. cumin

SP   – ½ tsp. ginger, pinch of black and cayenne pepper and (to taste) 4 crushed garlic cloves

SL   – salt

Leave it to rest for 30 min. Preheat the oven to the maximum temperature. Roast the chicken in an uncovered casserole for 20 min. Then reduce the temperature (140–150 °C), cover the casserole and roast for another 50 min.

Serve it with boiled potatoes or chips and stewed or boiled vegetables.

## Roast Chicken with Onion

S   – 6–8 pieces of chicken (small drumsticks or other parts) rub with:

B   – turmeric, 1 tsp. marjoram

SW  – 1 tbsp. olive oil

SP  – ½ tsp. ginger, pinch of black and cayenne pepper

SL  – salt

Leave it to rest for 30 min. Preheat the oven to the maximum temperature. Roast the chicken in an uncovered casserole for 20 min. Then reduce the temperature (140–150 °C), cover the chicken with slices of onion and garlic (4 large onions and 4 garlic cloves), sprinkle with pepper and salt, cover the casserole and roast for another 50 min.

Serve it with white bread or boiled potatoes.

## Roast Duck with Stuffing

S   – you need one whole duck; remove the neck and wings and rub the duck inside and outside with the following spices:

B   – turmeric

SW  – 1 tsp. olive oil

SP  – black and cayenne pepper, and pinch of nutmeg (but this one only inside)

SL  – salt (to taste)

Stuffing:

S   – mince 100 g of liver and 100 g of stomachs; add one bread roll soaked in water

Mix it all together and then add:

B    – pinch of turmeric and marjoram

SW  – 2 whisked eggs, 1 tbsp. melted butter

SP   – ¼ tsp. ginger, pinch of nutmeg, black and cayenne pepper (to taste)

SL   – salt (to taste)

S    – 1 tbsp. of chopped fresh parsley (the stuffing should not be too dense)

Stitch up the neck hole, stuff the duck with the stuffing and stitch up the other end. Preheat the oven to the maximum temperature. Place the duck in a casserole and roast uncovered for about 30 min. (the duck should be slightly golden). Then reduce the heat down to 140–150 °C, cover the casserole and roast the duck for another 2 hours.

## Roast Chicken with Stuffing

Use the same recipe as for the roast duck; only rub the chicken with some more ginger and pepper and roast it for 1½ instead of 2 hours.

## Roast Turkey with Stuffing

Use the same recipe as for the roast duck, only make some more stuffing and do not rub it with ginger but only with black pepper. The roasting time depends on the size of the turkey – on average 2½–3 hours.

## Fried Fish (fillets)

(you can use all kinds of fish, including carp)

SL   – ½ kg fish fillets

Rub each of the fillets with the following spices:

S    – some lemon juice

B    – pinch of turmeric and thyme

SW  – some oil

SP    – ginger, black and cayenne pepper

SL    – salt (to taste)

Leave them to rest for an hour. You can cover the fillets with breadcrumbs or flour or simply fry them plain.

Serve with boiled potatoes or chips and stewed carrots and/or horseradish.

## Fish in Vegetables

SL    – ½ kg fish fillets

Rub each of the fillets with the following spices:

S     – some lemon juice

B     – turmeric and thyme

SW   – some oil

SP    – ginger, black and cayenne pepper

SL    – salt (to taste)

Leave them to rest for an hour. Fry the fillets in a pan with some oil (6 tbsp.). Then place them in a casserole (without the oil) and add:

SW   – 1 large carrot, chopped

SW   – 2 onions, chopped in half rings

SP    – a small piece of cabbage, chopped

SP    – ½ tsp. ginger, white, black and cayenne pepper

SL    – add 100 ml of cold water, some salt (to taste); stir it all and stew for 10–15 min.

S     – add about 100 ml tomato juice (to taste), and pinch of basil

B     – pinch of turmeric and thyme

Stew it for another 5–10 min. If necessary you can thicken the sauce with some potato starch mixed with cold water. This dish should be rather spicy and hot. Serve it with boiled potatoes or bread.

# SIDE VEGETABLES

## Stewed Carrots

B    – to 1 200 ml of boiling water add:

SW   – 1 kg of diced carrots

SW   – ½ tsp. butter

SW   – ½ tsp. honey

SP   – pinch of white pepper and ginger (if you like you can also add 1 small finely chopped onion)

Cook it all together for 15 min. and then add:

SL   – salt (to taste)

S    – 1 tbsp. lemon juice

B    – pinch of turmeric

B    – add boiling water (if necessary) and cook it until soft

SW   – gently thicken it with some cold water mixed with potato starch, bring it to the boil and add ½ tsp. of butter

## Stewed Vegetables (carrots, peas and kohlrabi)

B    – to ½ l of boiling water add:

B    – pinch of thyme

SW   – ½ kg diced carrots

SW   – 1 tsp. butter

SP   – 3 diced kohlrabi

SP   – ½ tsp. ginger, pinch of white pepper

Cook it all together for 15 min. and then add:

SL   – salt (to taste)

S    – 1 tbsp. lemon juice

B    – pinch of turmeric

B    – add boiling water (if necessary)

SW  – add 100–200 g of green peas

Cook it all together until soft (around 15 min.). Add ½ tsp. of butter and, if you like, some honey too. Thicken it with some cold water mixed with potato starch.

You can use different variations of the vegetables, e.g. carrots and pea, carrots and kohlrabi or simply kohlrabi on its own.

## Beetroot Salad

SW  – grate 1 kg of boiled beetroots; then add:

SW  – 1 tsp. cumin

SW  – 1 tbsp. oil

SW  – 1–2 tsp. honey

Mix it all together and add:

SP   – 1 medium onion, finely chopped

SP   – pinch of white pepper

SL   – salt (to taste)

S    – juice of ½ a lemon or white wine vinegar (to taste)

B    – pinch of thyme

Mix it all together. The salad should have a sweet-sour flavour; if necessary, add some more of the spices (remember the order of the flavours).

## Beetroot with Horseradish

SW  – grate finely 1 kg of boiled beetroots; then add:

SW  – 1 tsp. honey

SP   – a jar (200 ml) of finely grated horseradish

SP   – pinch of white pepper

SL  – salt (to taste)

S   – if necessary, add some lemon juice

Mix it all together thoroughly.

## Warm Beetroots

SW  – grate finely 1 kg of boiled beetroots

SW  – prepare some roux in a casserole (2 tbsp. oil, 1 tbsp. butter, 2 tbsp. plain wheat flour)

SW  – add the beetroots to the roux and fry it all together, stirring constantly

SW  – add some honey (to taste)

SP  – pinch of ginger and white pepper

SL  – salt (to taste)

S   – some lemon juice (1–2 tbsp.)

Fry it all together on a medium heat for another 10–15 min.

## Stewed Sauerkraut with Button Mushrooms

S   – to ½ kg of very sour and not drained sauerkraut add:

B   – ½ l boiling water

B   – pinch of thyme and ⅓ tsp. turmeric

Cook it all together.

SW  – fry briefly, with 4 tbsp. of oil, 3 medium chopped onions; then add them to the sauerkraut together with the following ingredients:

SW  – ½ tsp. cumin and 2 juniper berries

SW  – 300 g of sliced button mushrooms

SW  – 5 medium carrots, grated

Mix it all together and then add:

SP  – ⅓ tsp. ginger, 4 grains allspice, 1 bay leaf, black and cayenne pepper (to taste)

SL  – salt (to taste)

Mix it all up thoroughly and stew it all together for 1 hour until soft.

## Cabbage and Carrot Salad

SW  – 1 large carrot, grated

SP  – ¼ medium size cabbage, finely chopped

SP  – 1 onion, finely chopped

SP  – white and black pepper (to taste)

SL  – salt (to taste)

Mix it all together and then add:

S  – some lemon juice (to taste)

S  – bunch of finely chopped parsley (optional)

B  – pinch of thyme

SW  – 1 tbsp. mayonnaise

SW  – ⅓ tsp. cumin

Mix it all together thoroughly.

## Cauliflower Salad

SP  – to 1 large, cauliflower, blanched and divided into small pieces, add:

SP  – white pepper

SP  – 2 garlic cloves, pressed

Mix it all together and then add:

SL  – salt (to taste)

S  – some lemon juice (the salad should be slightly sour)

B  – pinch of turmeric

SW  – 1–2 tsp. liquid honey, 1 tbsp. mayonnaise

If necessary, add some more of the spices (remember the order of the flavours).

## Stewed Cabbage with Tomatoes

B  – to ½ l of boiling water add pinch of thyme

SW  – fry briefly, with 3–4 tbsp. of oil, 3 large chopped onions; then add them to the boiling water together with the following ingredients:

SW  – ½ tsp. cumin

SP  – 1 medium cabbage, chopped

SP  – 3–4 garlic cloves

SP  – 4 grains allspice, ½ a bay leaf, ½ tsp. ginger, white and cayenne pepper

SL  – salt (to taste)

Mix it all together and cook for 20 min; then add:

S  – 3–4 very ripe tomatoes, peeled and chopped

Cook it all until soft. You can thicken it by adding and stirring in 1–2 tbsp. of plain wheat flour. At the end of cooking add:

B  – pinch of turmeric

SW  – ½ tsp. cumin

SP  – some pepper and salt (SL) to taste

## Stewed Courgette or Patison

SW  – 3 small courgettes (about 1 kg), finely diced (if necessary get rid of the seeds first); preheat 100 ml of oil (make sure the oil is very hot) and fry the courgettes for 2–3 min., then drain and place them in a casserole.

SW  – using the same oil, briefly fry 3 large chopped onions; then drain them, also place in the casserole and add:

SP  – ½ tsp. ginger, white and cayenne pepper (to taste)

SL  –100 ml cold water, salt (to taste)

Cook it all together and keep adding:

S  – 4 very ripe tomatoes, peeled and chopped, then fried with 1 tbsp. of oil

B  – pinch of turmeric and thyme

Stew it under cover until soft (about 15 min.)

SW – thicken it with some potato starch mixed with cold water

SP – add some pepper and salt (SL) to taste (the dish should be quite spicy)

Just before stewing you can also add one or two red peppers, chopped and fried with oil (SW).

## Stewed Sweet Pepper

Use the same recipe as for the stewed courgette but instead of courgette put as much pepper (SW) as you like. You can also mix the two vegetables together. In a similar way you can cook aubergines and courgettes.

## Red Cabbage Salad

B – chop 1 medium red cabbage and throw it to some boiling water; boil it for 2–3 min., then drain and cool it, place it in a bowl and add:

SW – 1 tbsp. oil, 1 tbsp. honey, 1 tsp. cumin

Mix it all up and keep adding:

SP – 1 large onion, finely chopped, pinch of black and white pepper and mix it again

SL – whilst mixing add some salt (to taste)

S – juice of ½ a lemon or some white wine vinegar (to taste)

B – pinch of thyme

If you think that the salad needs more flavour, simply add some more of the spices (remember the order of the flavours, though).

## Stewed Red Cabbage

B – to ½ l of boiling water with pinch of thyme add 1 medium red cabbage, finely chopped; whilst cooking keep adding the following ingredients:

SW – 1 tsp. butter, 1 tsp. honey

SP – 1 large onion, chopped

SP  – 4 cloves, 4 grains allspice, pinch of pepper

SL  – salt (to taste)

Stir it all together and stew for 15 min. Whilst stirring keep adding the following ingredients:

S  – about 3 tbsp. lemon juice (to taste)

B  – pinch of turmeric

Stew it all for 10 min. until soft.

SW – thicken it with some potato starch mixed with cold water; add 1 tsp. of butter and, if necessary, all the other spices (remember the order of the flavours).

## Stewed Vegetables

Choose the vegetables to taste; chop them and fry them for 2–3 min. one by one, separately (in the order of the flavours) in a very hot pan with some oil. Drain the vegetables and place in a casserole. For example:

SW – 2 medium carrots, chopped

SP – 1 large onion, chopped

SP – quarter of a cabbage, chopped

SP – add some white and black pepper (to taste), ¼ tsp. ginger

SL – add 100 ml of cold water, salt (to taste); stew it and add:

S – pinch of basil, some lemon juice or 1 large and ripe tomato, peeled and chopped

B – pinch of turmeric and thyme; stew it for 10 min.

SW – gently thicken it with some potato starch mixed with cold water

This type of a vegetable dish goes nicely with supper.

## Fried Vegetables

Choose the vegetables to taste; grate them or finely chop (e.g. cabbage). Fry them for 2–3 min. with some oil in a very hot pan, always one by one; then drain them and place in a casserole. For example:

SW  – 1 large carrot, grated

SP  – 2 large leeks (only the white parts), finely chopped

Mix it all together and add:

SP  – pinch of ginger and pepper

SL  – salt (to taste)

S  – ½ tsp. lemon juice

B  – pinch of turmeric and thyme

Fry it all together. Vegetables prepared this way go nicely with sandwiches and pasta and are good for stuffing meat (mostly chicken and pork).

## Canned Green Bean Salad

SL  – drain 1 can of green beans (you can use the brine in a soup) and place them in a bowl; keep mixing and adding the following ingredients and spices:

S  – 1 tbsp. lemon juice

B  – pinch of thyme

SW  – 1 tsp. honey

SP  – 1 medium onion, finely chopped

SP  – pinch of white pepper

SL  – salt (to taste)

## Canned Green Peas Salad

SW  – place 1 can of peas (together with the brine) into a casserole; warm it up on a hob and keep adding:

SW  – ½ tsp. butter

SP  – pinch of white pepper

SL   – pinch of salt

S    – 1 tsp. lemon juice

B    – pinch of turmeric

SW  – gently thicken it with some potato starch mixed with cold water

Bring it to the boil and cook for 1–2 min.

# SALADS FOR SUPPER

## Vegetable Salad with Marinated Pepper and Sweet Corn

SW  – to 3–4 carrots and 1 parsnip (or parsley root, if available) (both
vegetables previously boiled in a soup  and chopped) add:

SP   – a piece of boiled celeriac, chopped

SP   – 1 large onion, finely chopped

SP   – white, black and herbal pepper (to taste)

Keep mixing it all together and adding the following ingredients:

SL   – salt (to taste)

S    – 3 marinated sweet red peppers, chopped

B    – pinch of thyme

SW  – 1 can of sweet corn (without the brine)

SW  – 2 tbsp. mayonnaise

Mix it all up and, if necessary, add some more pepper (SP) and salt (SL).

## Vegetable Salad with Tomatoes

SW  – to 3–4 carrots and 1 parsnip (or parsley root, if available) (both
vegetables previously boiled in a soup and chopped) and 2 boiled eggs
(also chopped) add:

SP   – 2 medium onions, chopped

SP   – white, black and herbal pepper

Keep mixing it all together and adding the following ingredients:

SL   – salt (to taste)

S    – 2 large and ripe tomatoes, peeled and chopped

B   – pinch of turmeric and thyme

SW  – about 2 tbsp. mayonnaise

Mix it all up and, if necessary, add some more pepper (SP) and salt (SL).

## Chicory, Pepper and Radish Salad

SW  – to 2 sweet red peppers, chopped in strips, add:

SP   – 150 g white radish, chopped in thin strips

SP   – black and white pepper

Keep mixing it and adding the following ingredients:

SL   – salt (to taste)

B   – 2 chicory, chopped in thin strips (remove the bitter central part, though)

B   – pinch of turmeric

SW  – 2 tbsp. mayonnaise

Mix it all up and, if necessary, add some pepper (SP), salt (SL) and lemon juice (S).

## Reddish Salad

SW  – to 3 boiled eggs, chopped, add:

SP   – 2 large onions, chopped

SP   – 1 garlic clove, pressed

SP   – 2 bunches of reddish, chopped

SP   – white and black pepper (to taste)

Keep mixing it and adding the following ingredients:

SL   – salt (to taste)

S     – bunch of chopped fresh parsley

S     – 1 large and ripe tomato, peeled and chopped

B     – pinch of thyme

SW   – 1–2 tbsp. mayonnaise

Mix it all up and, if necessary, add some pepper (SP) and salt (SL).

## Cress and Lettuce Salad

SP    – 2 bunches of radish, chopped

SP    – bunch of cress, chopped

SP    – 1 garlic clove, pressed

SP    – white and black pepper (to taste)

Keep mixing it and adding the following ingredients:

SL    – salt (to taste)

S     – some lemon juice (to taste)

B     – one head of lettuce, torn

B     – pinch of thyme

SW   – 1 tbsp. mayonnaise

Mix it all up and, if necessary, add some pepper (SP), and salt (SL).

## Tomato and Lettuce Salad

SW – 4 boiled eggs, chopped

Keep mixing and adding the following ingredients:

SP    –bunch of chives, chopped or 1 onion, chopped

SP    – 1 garlic clove, pressed

SP    – white, black and herbal pepper (to taste)

SL    – salt (to taste)

S     – 2 ripe tomatoes, peeled and chopped

B    – one head of lettuce, torn

B    – pinch of turmeric

SW  – 1–2 tbsp. mayonnaise

Mix it all up and, if necessary, add some more pepper (SP) and salt (SL).

## Pea Salad I

SW  – 3 boiled eggs, chopped

SW  – 1 can of peas, drained

Keep mixing it and adding the following ingredients:

SP    – bunch of radish, chopped

SP    – bunch of chives, chopped or 1 onion, chopped

SP    – 1 garlic clove, pressed

SP    – black and white pepper

SL    – salt (to taste)

S      – bunch of chopped fresh parsley

S      – some lemon juice (to taste)

B      – a few leaves of lettuce, torn

B      – pinch of turmeric

SW   – 1–2 tbsp. mayonnaise

Mix it all up and, if necessary, add some more pepper (SP) and salt (SL).

## Pea Salad II

SW  – 1 can of peas, drained

Keep mixing it and adding the following ingredients:

SP    – 1 large onion, chopped

SP    – black and white pepper (to taste)

SL    – salt (to taste)

S   – 1 medium gherkin, grated

B   – pinch of turmeric and thyme

SW  – 1 tbsp. mayonnaise

Mix it all up and, if necessary, add some more pepper (SP) and salt (SL).

## Egg Salad (*Paste*)

SW  – 5 boiled eggs, finely chopped

Keep mixing it and adding the following ingredients:

SP  – 2 onions, finely chopped

SP  – white, black and herbal pepper (to taste)

SP  – 1 tsp. mustard

SL  – salt (to taste)

S   – 1 bigger gherkin, finely grated

B   – pinch of turmeric

SW  – 1–2 tbsp. mayonnaise

Mix it all up and, if necessary, add some more pepper (SP) and salt (SL). The paste should be quite spicy in flavour.

## Traditional Vegetable Salad

To boiling water keep adding (in the following order) washed but unpeeled vegetables: 6 large carrots, 2 large parsnips (or parsley roots, if available), 1 medium celeriac, 500 g potatoes (boil them separately).

Boil then peel the vegetables. Chop them finely, keep mixing them and adding the following ingredients:

SW  – 1 tbsp. salad oil

SW  – 3 boiled eggs, chopped

SP  – 2 medium onions, chopped

SP  – 1–2 tbsp. mustard

SP  – black, white and herbal pepper (to taste)

SL  – salt (to taste)

S  – bunch of chopped fresh parsley

B  – pinch of turmeric

SW  – a jar of mayonnaise (300 ml)

Mix it all up and, if necessary, add some more pepper (SP), mustard (SP) and salt (SL). Leave the salad to rest before serving.

## Tuna or Sardine Salad

SL  – mash up with a fork 1 can of tuna or sardines (together with the brine)

Keep mixing it and adding the following ingredients:

S  – a few drops of lemon juice

S  – 1 tsp. mustard

B  – pinch of turmeric

SW  – 2 boiled eggs, chopped

SW  – 1 tbsp. mayonnaise

SP  – 1 large onion, chopped

SP  – black and white pepper (to taste)

SP  – 1 tsp. mustard

SL  – salt (to taste)

Mix it all up and make sure that the salad is spicy enough.

## Smoked Mackerel Salad (Paste)

SL  – mince 1 large mackerel, boneless and skinless

Keep mixing it and adding the following ingredients:

S  – a few drops of lemon juice or 1 tsp. mustard

B      – pinch of turmeric and thyme

SW   – 1 tbsp. mayonnaise

SP    – 1 large onion, chopped

SP    – white and black pepper (to taste)

SL    – salt (to taste)

Mix it all up thoroughly. The paste should be quite spicy. It is even tastier with some smoked halibut added to it.

## SUPPER DISHES

### Hungarian-style Sausage

SW   – fry gently, with 2 tbsp. of oil, 3 large onions, chopped; place them in a casserole and add:

SW   – ½ tsp. cumin

SP    – ½ tsp. ginger, pinch of cayenne pepper, ¼ tsp. coriander

SP    – 2 garlic cloves, pressed

Mix it all up.

SL    – fry with 1 tbsp. of oil 600 g of cut in half sausages; place them in the casserole, add 100 ml of cold water and some salt (to taste)

Stew it all together for 20 min. Then add:

SL    – 1 can of green beans with the brine

S      – about 200 ml tomato juice

B      – ⅓ tsp. turmeric and thyme

Stew it for another 10 min.

SW   – gently thicken it with some potato starch mixed with cold water and, if necessary, add some more pepper (SP) and salt (SL). This dish should be quite spicy and goes best with white bread.

## Sweet Corn Sauce (for pasta)

SW – fry with 1 tbsp. of oil 1 can of sweet corn (without the brine); place in a casserole, add the brine and keep adding the following ingredients:

SW – 2 large onions, chopped and fried with 2 tbsp. of oil

SP – 3 garlic cloves, pressed

SP – ½ tsp. ginger, pinch of black and cayenne pepper, ⅓ tsp. coriander

SL – 1 sausage, cut in half and 200 g of bacon, cut in stripes, fried with 1 tbsp. of oil

SL – 200 ml of cold water

SL – salt (to taste)

Stir it all up, stew on a hob and keep adding:

S – 1 tsp. lemon juice, pinch of basil and bunch of chopped fresh parsley

Stew it for about 15 min.

SW – gently thicken the sauce with some potato starch mixed with cold water

The sauce should be quite spicy.

## Pizza

Dough:

S – 400 g plain wheat flour

B – ¼ tsp. turmeric

SW – 7 tbsp. oil

SP – ½ tsp. ginger

SL – pinch of salt

S – 50 g of yeast mixed with 2 tbsp. of lukewarm water

Knead the dough, slowly adding the lukewarm water. Roll out the dough and place on a baking try (smeared with some fat). Cover it up and leave in a warm place for 30 min. Then smear the dough with oil and top it with:

S      – 4 ripe tomatoes, peeled and cut into slices

B      – some thyme

SW    – ½ kg of sliced, fried and seasoned button mushrooms

SW    – 3 large onions, cut into slices and gently fired

SP     – sprinkle some ginger, black and cayenne pepper, oregano

SL     – salt

SL     – few slices of ham, sausage or bacon

S      – 200 g of grated cheese

S      – sprinkle some basil

B      – and marjoram

Preheat the oven to 170 °C. Bake the pizza for about 1 hour.

## Tartare Sauce

(serve with cold meat and fish in jelly)

SW    –  to 2 boiled egg yolks, chopped and 1 raw egg yolk add:

SP     – 2 tbsp. mustard

SL     – pinch of salt

S      – 1 tsp. lemon juice

B      – ¼ tsp. turmeric

SW    – slowly pour ½ l of sunflower seed or soya oil to the mixture and keep
           whisking it all the time; then slowly pour 100 ml boiling water (do not
           stop whisking); keep whisking and adding:

SW    – boiled egg whites, finely chopped

SP     – white, black and cayenne pepper (to taste)

SP     – 1 medium onion, finely chopped

SL     – salt (to taste)

S      – 300 ml of marinated button mushrooms, finely chopped

S      – 300 ml of gherkins, finely chopped

B    – pinch of turmeric and thyme

SW   – if necessary add some mayonnaise

SP   – and some pepper and salt (SL)

The sauce should be rather spicy.


## Ham Hock in Jelly

B    – to some boiling water add:

B    – pinch of thyme

SW   – 1 tsp. cumin

SP   – 1 tsp. ginger

SL   – 1 big ham hock

SL   – 1 tsp. salt

S    – ⅓ tsp. basil

B    – ¼ tsp. turmeric

Cook it all together for 3 hours and then add:

SW   – 3 whole carrots and 1 parsnip (or parsley root, if available)

SP   – ½ a celeriac, 4 whole garlic cloves, pinch of cayenne pepper, 5 grains allspice, 1 bay leaf

SL   – 1½ tsp. salt

S    – bunch of greens

B    – pinch of marjoram

Cook it all together for another 1½ hours (at the end of cooking there should be about 2 1 of stock left).

Take the ham hock out of the casserole, remove the bones and press the meat tightly into a small bowl, so once it is cold it acquires the shape of the bowl. Cool it in a fridge. In the stock, dilute an appropriate quantity of gelatine (SW) and, if necessary, add some pepper (SP), salt (SL) and the following ingredients:

S    – about 200 ml of white wine

B    – pinch of thyme

B    – add boiling water (if necessary)

SW   – 2 whisked egg whites (to make the stock clearer)

Boil it all together for 30 min. Then strain the stock through a cloth.

Cut the cold ham hock in half and then slice it into small pieces. Place them neatly on a big plate together with the boiled and finely chopped vegetables. Then pour the stock all over the meat and leave it to set. Serve with some tartare sauce.

## Homemade Pâté

B    – to 3 l of boiling water add:

B    – pinch of thyme

SW   – 500 g boneless beef

SW   – ½ tsp. cumin

SP   – 5 large onions, 1 tsp. ginger, 5 grains allspice, 1 bay leaf

SL   – 500 g boneless pork, 1 kg raw pancetta

Cook it all together on a low heat for 4 hours; do not add water. Then add:

SL   – 500 g pork liver

S    – 500 g chicken liver

Cook it for another hour (meat should be well cooked and not much stock left). Take the meat out of the stock and cool it down. Soak in the stock 2 dry bread rolls. Then mince the meat and the bread rolls and add:

B    – ¼ tsp. turmeric, 1 tsp. marjoram

SW   – 4 egg yolks

SW   – 4 egg whites, whisked

SP   – 2 tsp. ginger, ½ a freshly grated nutmeg, ⅓ tsp. cayenne pepper, 1 tsp. coriander, black and herbal pepper, to taste (the pâté should be quite spicy)

SL  – some salt (to taste)

S  – 1 tsp. basil

S  – 1 tbsp. lemon juice

Mix it all together thoroughly and, if necessary, add some more spices (remember the order of the flavours). Smear a deep baking tray with some fat and sprinkle it with breadcrumbs. Place the pâté in the tray and bake it in the oven for about 2 hours (180 °C).

## Lard with Spices

SL  – melt on a low heat 1 kg of finely chopped pork fat; when the cracklings are golden and crispy you can start adding the following spices:

S  – 2 tbsp. basil

B  – 1 tbsp. thyme, 2 tbsp. marjoram, ¼ tsp. turmeric

SW  – ½ tsp. cumin

SP  – 2 tsp. ginger, 1 tsp. cayenne pepper, 1 tsp. black pepper

Cool it down, stirring. When half-set, pour the lard into glass jars (this way the spices and the cracklings will not go down to the bottom).

# CAKES

## Chocolate Sponge Cake

SW  – whisk 5 whole eggs with 225 g of sugar and some vanilla sugar; then stir it with a wooden spoon and keep adding the following ingredients:

SP  – 1 tsp. ginger

SL  – pinch of salt

S  – 200 ml of plain wheat flour mixed with 1 flat tsp. of baking powder

B  – 1½ tsp. cocoa

SW  – 100 g potato starch

SW  – 200 g butter, melted

Preheat the oven to 170 °C. Grease a deep baking tin and sprinkle it with breadcrumbs. Pour the mixture into the tin and bake for 70 min. Let the cake cool for a while. Then remove it from the tin and top it with melted chocolate and some chopped walnuts.

## Yellow Sponge Cake

SW – beat 6 eggs into a bowl; then place the bowl over a saucepan of simmering water and whisk the eggs with 300 g of sugar and some vanilla sugar; cool the mixture down, stir it with a wooden spoon and keep adding the following ingredients:

SP   – 1 tsp. ginger, 2 tbsp. rectified spirit

SL   – pinch of salt

S    – 6 tbsp. plain wheat flour mixed with 1 tsp. of baking powder

B    – ⅓ tsp. turmeric

SW  – 6 tbsp. sunflower seed oil

SW  – 300 g potato starch

Stir it all together and then add:

SW – 200 g butter, melted

Gently stir it all until thoroughly combined. Preheat the oven to 170 °C. Grease a large, deep tin and sprinkle it with breadcrumbs. Pour the mixture into the tin and bake it for 1 hour.

Let the cake cool and (if you like) top it with melted chocolate and some chopped walnuts.

## Coconut Cake

### *Sponge cake:*

SW – beat 6 eggs into a bowl; then place the bowl over a saucepan of simmering water and whisk the eggs with 6 tbsp. of sugar and some vanilla sugar; cool it down and then add 6 tbsp. of potato starch and gently stir it in with a wooden spoon; then add:

SP    – 1 tsp. ginger

SL    – pinch of salt and 1 tsp. baking powder

Stir the mixture until thoroughly combined. Preheat the oven to 150–160 °C. Line a baking tin with some greased paper. Pour the mixture into the tin and bake it for 40 min.

### *Cream:*

Cook 1 pack of custard with 6 tbsp. of sugar. Let it cool

SW    – whisk 340 g of butter adding from time to time a spoonful of the custard; then add:

SP    – 4 tbsp. rectified spirit

SL    – pinch of salt

S    – 1 tbsp. lemon juice

Cut the sponge cake across in the middle into two parts. Spread ¾ of the cream evenly on the bottom half; then top it with the other half of the cake and spread the rest of the cream on top of the cake.

### *Coconut Topping:*

Preheat in a big non-stick pan 3 heaped tbsp. of butter with 4 tbsp. of sugar. Then add 200 g of coconut flakes and pinch of ginger. Fry it gently, stirring all the time, until the mixture acquires a lightly golden colour (do not burn it). Let it cool for a while. Spread the lukewarm mixture on top of the cake.

## Birthday Cake

*Sponge cake:*

SW – beat 7 eggs into a bowl; then place the bowl over a saucepan of simmering water and whisk the eggs with 150 g of sugar; let it cool and then gently stir in with a wooden spoon:

SP  – ½ tsp. ginger

SL  – pinch of salt

S   – 150 g plain wheat flour

B   – ⅓ tsp. turmeric

Preheat the oven to 160 °C. Grease a round baking tin (25 cm diameter) and sprinkle it with breadcrumbs. Stir the mixture until thoroughly combined. Pour the mixture into the tin and bake for 50 min. Let it cool; then cut it across into three equal rings and soak them with some punch.

*Punch:*

Mix in a saucepan:

S   – juice of 2 lemons

B   – pinch of turmeric

SW  – 4 tbsp. sugar

Bring it to the boil then let it cool. When nearly cold add to it:

SP  – 100 ml of rum or cognac or vodka and stir it

*Cream:*

Beat two eggs in a bowl; then place the bowl over a saucepan of simmering water and whisk the eggs with 150 g of sugar; let it cool.

SW  – whisk 400 g of butter with the following ingredients:

SW  – the whisked eggs, spoon by spoon

SP  – 4 tbsp. rectified spirit or cognac or rum

SL   – pinch of salt

S    – 1 tbsp. lemon juice

S    – 300 ml black cherry or blackcurrant jam (best homemade)

Spread most of the mixture on the bottom and the middle rings of the cake. Put all three rings one on top of the other and spread the rest of the cream all around the cake. Top it with some melted chocolate and decorate with chopped walnuts and other confectionery.

## Ginger Bread à la Granny Sophie

SW   – whisk 5 whole eggs with 150 g of sugar; keep whisking and slowly pour 200 ml of liquid honey and 200 ml of sunflower oil

SP   – mix 1 bag of ginger bread spice with 1 tsp. of ginger; slowly add it to the egg mixture together with:

SL   – pinch of salt

S    – 600 g of plain wheat flour mixed with 1 tsp. of bicarbonate of soda and 1 tsp. of baking powder

S    – 200 ml of kefir or sour milk

B    – 1 tbsp. cocoa

B    – 200 g walnuts, chopped

SW   – 300 g dates, chopped

Mix it all together until properly combined. Preheat the oven to 160–170 °C. Line a deep baking tin with some greased paper. Pour the mixture into the tin and bake it for 1 hour.

## Apple Cake

SW – whisk 4 eggs with 200 g of sugar; keep whisking and slowly add:

SW – 150 g butter, melted

Then stir it gently with a wooden spoon and add:

SW – ½ tsp. cinnamon

SP – 1 flat tbsp. ginger

SL – pinch of salt

S – 200 g of plain wheat flour mixed with 2 flat tsp. of baking powder

B – ⅓ tsp. turmeric

Preheat the oven to 180 °C. Grease a round baking tin (25 cm diameter) and sprinkle it with breadcrumbs. Stir the mixture thoroughly until properly combined. Pour the mixture into the tin and dip into it around 7–8 whole apples (only peeled and seeded). Bake it for 1½ hours.

## Strawberry Cake

S      – mix 400 g of plain wheat flour with:

B      – ½ tsp. turmeric

SW   – 150 g butter

SW   – 3 tbsp. icing sugar

SW   – 2 eggs

Mix it all up and then add:

SP    – 2 tsp. ginger

SL    – pinch of salt

S      – 50 g of yeast diluted in 2 tbsp. of lukewarm water or sour cream

Preheat the oven to 170 °C. Line a baking tin with some greased paper. Knead the dough, then roll it out and put it into the tin. Leave it for 30 min. to rise in a warm place. Wash some ripe, medium-sized strawberries. Dry them and place them upside down on top of the dough. Bake the cake for 1 hour, checking on it from time to time. Once baked, remove the cake from the oven and, whilst still hot, sprinkle it with some icing sugar. This cake is best served warm.

## Spicy Honey Balls

Melt in a saucepan 600 g of honey (rapeseed honey is best in this case). Preheat the oven to a medium temperature. Place on a baking tray 500 g of oats and put them in the oven. Leave them to dry for 15–20 min. Stir the oats from time to time until dry and crispy. (You can also do this in a frying pan.)

Into a 2 l saucepan put:

B    – 8–9 tsp. cocoa; then add constantly stirring:

SW  – the melted honey

SW  – ⅓ tsp. cinnamon

SP   – ¼ tsp. ginger

Cook for 1–2 min. Then take it off the hob and stir in the oats until thoroughly combined with the honey. Then transfer the mixture onto two flat plates. Let it cool for a while, and whilst still slightly warm, form the mixture into small balls (1 or 2 cm diameter).

The spicy honey balls are very gentle on the stomach and the intestines and can successfully replace sweets both for kids and adults.

# TEA, COFFEE, COCOA

*(serve all teas in a glass pot)*

## Neutral Tea I (good for everyone)

B    – to 1½ l of boiling water add:

B    – ½ tsp. thyme

SW  – 1 tsp. liquorice

SP   – pinch of ginger

Bring it to the boil and simmer for 2–3 min.

## Neutral Tea II (good for everyone)

SL  – to 1½ l of cold water add:

S  – 1 tbsp. forest berries tea; bring it to the boil and then add:

B  – ½ tsp. thyme

SW  – ½ tsp. liquorish

SW  – ½ tsp. aniseed

SP  – pinch of ginger

Bring it to the boil and simmer for 2–3 min.

## Date Tea

B  – to 1½ l of boiling water add:

SW  – 1 tbsp. liquorice

SW  – 5–6 dried dates

SP  – ¼ tsp. cinnamon

SP  – ¼ tsp. ginger

Bring it to the boil and simmer for 5 min. This tea is particularly good in autumn and winter. If necessary, you can increase the amount of particular ingredients.

## Boiled Coffee

Pour into a saucepan the required amount of water. Bring it to the boil, reduce the heat and add 1–2 tsp. natural grained coffee. Bring it to the boil and simmer for 1–2 min. Drink it with some honey.

Boiled coffee and the 'killer' tea (see recipe) are especially recommended for the side effects of overeating sweets, fruit, fruit juices and cheeses.

## Boiled Cocoa

To 200 ml of boiled water add 1–2 tsp. of cocoa. Bring it to the boil and simmer for 2 min. You can also add some milk and honey.

# PRESERVES

Over the summer and autumn you can make your own homemade preserves. Use only ripe and sweet fruit. In our climate, apricots, plums and pears are best for this purpose. Apricots and plums are best in jams and pears in compotes. In order to diversify your autumn and winter menu you can also preserve some vegetables. They are especially good for those days when you are too busy to cook something from scratch. For any food preserves you should only use natural honey, white wine vinegar and natural spices.

If the fruit is very sour and requires a large amount of sugar, then you should simply not use it for any preserves. We should not cheat our taste buds with sugar. Preserves with large amounts of sugar, even if made from the most wonderful fruit, will not be of any benefit to our health during the winter time.

You should make the vegetable preserves according to your favourite recipes. You need only remember that instead of sugar you use honey, instead of acetic acid vinegar you use white wine vinegar, and you should always use large amounts of spices.

Do not make too many pickles, though, because you should not be eating too much sour food anyway.

## Plum Jam

Pit 5 kg of sweet plums. Place them in a saucepan with a thick bottom. Preheat the oven to 180 °C. Cover the saucepan and put into the oven for 1–2 hours for the plums to sweat. Then take the cover off the saucepan and stir the plums, letting the steam out. Do this until the plum mixture starts thickening.

Then take the saucepan out of the oven, place it on a hob, keep stirring and adding the following ingredients: 4 tbsp. honey (SW), 1 tsp. cinnamon (SW), 1 tsp. ginger (SP) and ½ tsp. salt (the salt makes the taste a bit milder).

Cook it on the hob for another hour, constantly stirring with a wooden spoon. Pasteurize some glass jars in the oven. Also, wipe each of the screw-top lids with some rectified spirit. Pour the jam into the jars and close them tightly. You do not need to boil the jars.

## Plum and Banana Jam

Slice 2 kg of very ripe bananas. Place them in a saucepan and cover with a lid. Put them into a preheated oven and let them steam for 1–2 hours. They should be very mushy; if they are not, then you can stew them for a little bit longer or simply blend them with a blender.

Add the banana mixture to the plum jam (see recipe) but before adding the honey. Then follow the rest of the recipe above.

## Apricot Jam

Use the same recipe as for the plum jam. Make sure that the apricots are very ripe and sweet, otherwise the jam will not be as tasty as it should be.

## Pear Compote

Peel some ripe and sweet pears. Cut them into halves and remove their seeds. Place them in large glass jars. To each of the jars (900 ml) add: ½ tsp. cinnamon and 4 cloves. Mix some boiled water with lemon juice and some honey. Pour the water into the jars. Close them tightly and boil them in a water bath for 15 min.

## Whole Tomatoes

Steam and then peel very ripe but still quite hard small tomatoes. Place them in large glass jars. To each of the jars (900 ml) add: ½ tsp. marjoram, ½ tsp. cumin, 1 slice of onion, 1 bay leaf, 5 grains allspice. Pour some boiling hot and salty water into the jars. Close them tightly and boil in a water bath for about 10 min.

These tomatoes go nicely in salads, pizzas, soups and sauces or on their own.

# RECIPES FOR WARMING AND STRENGTHENING DISHES

With each of these recipes we may experience some unwanted side effects, such as itchy rashes on our hands and itchy or red eyes. These are not very dangerous. However, if we spot any of these side effects we should stop eating this type of food immediately and drink ½ glass of water with lemon juice or eat a slice of white cheese. This situation may occur when we drastically change our diet. Our body is simply not ready to absorb so much of the warming factor. We should not use these recipes during antibiotic and hormonal treatments.

## Beef Broth

B  – to 2–3 l of boiling water add:

B  – ½ tsp. thyme and ¼ tsp. turmeric

SW  – 800 g beef on the bone

SW  – ½ tsp. cumin

Cook it all together for 2 hours and then add:

SW  – 3 medium carrots, cut in half

SW  – 1 parsnip (or parsley root, if available), cut in half

SP  – 1 large onion, 2 garlic cloves, ½ tsp. ginger, pinch of cayenne pepper, 1 bay leaf, 4 grains allspice

SL  – salt (to taste)

Cook it for another hour until all soft.

Serve it with potatoes, cornmeal, egg noodles or couscous. Eat it only when feeling very cold or weakened.

## Lamb Broth

B  – to 2–3 l of boiling water add:

B  – ½ tsp. thyme, ¼ tsp. turmeric

B  – 700 g young lamb on the bone

SW  – ½ tsp. cumin

Cook it all together for 2 hours and then add:

SW  – 3 medium carrots, cut in half

SW  – 1 parsnip (or parsley root, if available), cut in half

SP  – a piece of celeriac

SP  – 1 onion, 3 garlic cloves, ½ tsp. ginger, 4 grains allspice, 1 bay leaf

SL  – salt (to taste)

Cook it for another hour until everything is soft.

Serve it with potatoes, cornmeal, egg noodles and couscous. Eat it only when feeling very cold or weakened.

## Energizing Beef Broth

B  – to 4 l of boiling water add:

B  – 1 tsp. thyme

SW  – 200 g of calf's bones with marrow or beef on the bone

SW  – 1 egg yolk

SW  – 1 carrot, chopped

Simmer it under cover for 6 hours (do not add water!). Store the broth in the fridge. It is very good to strengthen the spleen and kidneys.

## Energizing Lamb Broth

B    – to 4 l of boiling water add:

B    – ½ kg of young lamb on the bone

B    – 1 tsp. angelica

SW   – pinch of cumin

SP   – 1 tsp. ginger

Simmer it under cover for 6 hours (do not add water!). Drink one cup three times a day for three days. Store the broth in the fridge. It is very good to strengthen the spleen and kidneys.

## Stewed Lamb

Rub young and lean lamb with some turmeric, cumin, ginger, garlic and salt. Preheat the oven to the maximum temperature. Place the meat in an uncovered casserole and put it into the oven. Roast the meat for 20 min. Then cover the casserole, reduce the heat to the minimum temperature and stew the meat until soft.

Serve in small portions with vegetables and potatoes. It mostly strengthens the spleen and kidneys.

## Beef Stewed in Red Wine

Chop 1 kg of boneless beef into small portions. Put it in a bowl with ½ l of red wine. Leave it in the fridge to soak for a day. Then add 1 chopped carrot, ½ tsp. ginger, 1 bay leaf, 3 grains allspice, 1 medium chopped onion and some salt (to taste) and simmer it all together under cover for 2 hours until all soft.

Serve it in small portions with bread rolls or potatoes. It mostly strengthens the spleen and kidneys.

## Stewed Carrot

B    – to 200 ml of boiling water add:

B    – pinch of turmeric

SW   – ½ kg carrots, chopped

SW   – 1 tsp. honey

SW   – 1 tsp. butter

SP    – ¼ tsp. ginger

SL    – salt (to taste)

Stew it under cover for 20 min. It is especially good for weakened stomach and kidneys.

## Carrot Soup

B    – to 2 l of boiling water add:

SW   – ½ kg carrots, chopped

Cook it for 1 hour until soft and then blend it.

Give it to children and adults suffering from intestinal problems as well as from diarrhoea, intestinal crumps and indigestion.

## Fried Garlic

Press 5 large garlic cloves into a pan with 1 tbsp. of olive oil. Add some pepper, some salt and fry it briefly.

Serve it on buttered bread with some white cheese. Eat it for breakfast for 3 days.

It is a great remedy for colds, flu and has generally strengthening properties.

## The 'Killer' Warming Tea

B   – to 300 ml boiling water add:

B   – 1 heaped tsp. thyme

SW  – 2 tsp. liquorice

SP  – ½ tsp. ginger

Simmer it for 5–10 min.

Drink it straight away after preparation and 30 min. or 1 hour before any meal. This tea is highly warming and great for stomach aches, flatulence, nausea and colds. Do not drink it during antibiotic or hormonal treatments or when you are suffering from any of the heat problems (*fire*).

## Ginger Tea

B   – to 200 ml of boiling water add:

SP  – 1 tsp. ginger

Simmer it for 3 min. Drink it slowly in small sips. The tea helps with liver stalling caused by stress, as well as with the effects of overeating or overcooling.

## Boiled Coffee with Ginger (Cinnamon or Cardamom)

B   – to 200 ml of boiling water add:

B   – 1 tsp. natural coffee

SP  – ¼ tsp. ginger

Drink the coffee with some honey. It is great for tiredness, the effects of overcooling or side effects of eating too many sweets.

## Red Indian's 'Drink of Life'

To 200 ml of boiling water add 1 tsp. of cocoa, ½ a vanilla pod and 1–4 tsp. of cayenne pepper. Simmer it for 3 min. It prevents flu and colds.

## Grog

Pour 150 ml of very hot black tea into a saucepan. Add 1 tsp. of lemon juice, 1 tsp. of honey and 50 ml of rum or cognac.

Drink it when you feel very cold and go immediately to bed. This tea will not work if you feel weak and apathetic (*cold liver*).

## Goat's Milk

To 200 ml of very hot goat's milk add ½ tsp. of butter (preferably clarified butter), 1 tsp. of honey and 1 large garlic clove, pressed.

Drink it before going to bed. It is a great remedy for colds and flu.

# SUGGESTIONS FOR BREAKFASTS, DINNERS AND SUPPERS

## Breakfast

### What can we eat for breakfast?

Our breakfasts should be diverse and always warm. We should choose what is best for us and what we like the most. We can eat various breakfast soups, different kinds of bread, toasts, jams (preferably homemade), white cheese with cream and pepper, boiled eggs, eggs with bacon, ketchup (preferably homemade), tomatoes and radish (in season), chives, vegetable salads, warm ham and sausages and warm pâtés. Ham, sausages and pâtés should always be eaten with a bit of mustard.

Try not to drink anything with your breakfast. Such drinks as natural coffee, chicory coffee or teas we should drink first, after we wake up.

## What should not we eat for breakfast?

We should avoid eating fresh fruit, fruit yogurts, fresh salads and too much cheese and drinking fruit juices and milk.

## Dinner

### Always remember:

- Do not mix chicken and fish with pasta, sour soups, fresh salads, fresh fruit, pickled gherkins, sauerkraut and sweets.

- Do not mix meat dishes with fresh salads and cold drinks.

- You can mix fresh salads with potatoes and grains, but never with meat.

- Do not mix beans and soya beans with sauerkraut, gherkins, fresh salads, fresh fruit, chicken, fish and sweets.

- Grains and rice should always be cooked in the oven.

- We can cook enough dinner for two days; as long as it is stored in the fridge it will not lose any of its nutritional value.

- We do not always have to cook two courses; we can eat one of the courses for supper. Especially for small kids, a thick vegetable soup is much more important than a second course.

### Examples of dinner menu

- Vegetable soup, roast pork, potatoes, beetroot salad, boiled cauliflower.

- Bean soup, pancakes with meat-veg stuffing.

- Ukrainian borscht, roast beef, green bean salad, stewed carrot, potatoes.

- Sweet cabbage soup, risotto.

- Split pea soup, pasta, spicy meat-veg stew.

- Tomato soup, spicy pork ribs, potatoes, stewed vegetables (carrots, kohlrabi and pea).

- Small round noodles soup, grains with rice, chicken breast with pepper.

- Vegetable soup based on a stock on the bone, pancakes with sweet stuffing.

- Blended leek soup, pasta (noodles), beef or veal stewed with vegetables, boiled cauliflower.

- Beef and chicken broth with pasta, chicken in white sauce, rice or potatoes, stewed carrots.

- Autumn soup, potato pancakes.

- Pearl barley soup with some meat, gnocchi with white cheese.

- Spring soup, chicken with onion, potatoes, stewed carrots.

- Sour rye soup with potatoes, boiled egg and sausage.

- Button mushroom soup, mince balls, potatoes, boiled cauliflower or cabbage.

- Golden soup (blended), beef with cabbage, potatoes.

- Onion soup without croutons, roast loin of pork, sauerkraut with button mushrooms, mash potatoes.

- Roast chicken, chips from the oven, stewed carrots, Brussels sprouts with butter.

- Chicken with pineapple and rice, sausage with green beans and bread rolls.

- Sweet corn soup, roast meat or meat from a broth, green béchamel sauce, pasta, green beans or cauliflower.

- Soup à la Napolitana, breaded chicken, potatoes, fried beetroot salad, cauliflower.

- Split pea soup with egg noodles, fried fish, potatoes, stewed carrots, horseradish.

## Supper

### What should we eat for supper?

We can eat anything we want except for fresh fruit and fresh salads, sour salads, sour soups, cheeses, fruit yogurts and sweets. We can eat mild vegetable salads, warm hams and sausages, fish pastes, eggs, meat sandwiches with some onion and black pepper, all kinds of warm dishes, pizza and meat jelly.

In the evening, and especially just before going to bed, we should avoid cold drinks.

# SUMMARY

Dear Readers, it may feel that after reading this book you have ended up with the impression of being back to square one. But it could also be that your newly gained consciousness will enable you to break through the jigsaw puzzle of your present life, which you have so intricately put together out of the commonly approved beliefs, habits, orders, stereotypes, truths and dogmas. At first, you may feel a little in despair, as you will find yourself out of your comfort zone. You may even experience a feeling of emptiness. But believe me, this feeling can be a very positive sign.

With time, you will decide to compose a new pattern to your life, and this time you will do so consciously and rather carefully. You will realize that you really want this to happen and that this path is the only right one for you; that there is no other alternative. In order to make this new life solid and stable you will have to acquire and adopt this newly gained knowledge in your everyday life.

Start living according to the rules from this book, but do not set your expectations too high. Simply observe yourself and make notes of everything that makes you feel bad or good, as well as all of your doubts and questions. You will be able to answer them with time.

You must remember that there will be moments when you will start losing your enthusiasm and energy; that talking to people with different viewpoints or with limited perception will make you feel disempowered and hopeless. But you must never try to change them or convince them of your opinions. Everything around us has its own time. Therefore, let those people experience things for themselves. You can give them advice or help them, but only when they ask you. Otherwise you will start living their suffering and problems. Of course, it is always different with members of your own family and the people you feel responsible for.

Once you start exploring the knowledge and experiences outlined in this book, you will be able to understand all those questions and issues that initially seemed impossible to comprehend. You have got to let yourself do this; you must want to understand how to live life honestly and fully.

However, do not expect a ready-made recipe for it. Everyone has to work out their own rules according to the state of their consciousness. You cannot speed up or slow down any of the processes. If you really want this to happen it will happen in its own time. Trust yourself and stay calm. It is absolutely normal that some people understand and adopt these rules quite quickly, whilst others need some time to chew through them and some people are never able to do this.

**In order to make things easier for you, I list here all the most important rules:**

Remember: *Regardless of who is the father of a disease – a bad diet is certainly its mother.* (Chinese proverb)

- Be careful with everything that is claimed to be healthy – it may be harmful for you.

- Be conscious of the climate you live in.

- Your body needs a different diet from those typical of California, the Mediterranean countries, India or Australia.

- The climate in most of Europe requires the food to be warming throughout the whole year.

- Fruit should be eaten in moderation and only in season.

- Do not mix sugar with fruit; if you think it is too sour for you, you should not eat it at all.

- Remember that adding sugar to fruit compotes or jams you will not get rid of the sour flavour (for example, in strawberry or gooseberry jam). By adding sugar you will merely augment the cooling nature of your preserves.

- Do not mix fruit (and especially citruses) with milk; such a combination will damage your spleen and liver.

- Citruses and other exotic fruit are of a strongly cooling and refreshing nature; thus, they are of benefit only to people living in a hot climate.

- Fruit yogurts do not have much to do with a healthy diet; they acidify the body and damage the spleen and liver.

- Natural yogurt is of a cooling nature and can be mixed only with food of a warming nature (as is done in Mediterranean cuisine).

- Remember that chicken is of a cooling nature; eaten in excess it can cool the body and damage the liver (cirrhosis). It should be eaten only occasionally and served with other food products.

- Pork also has a cooling nature and eaten in excess damages the kidneys. You should always cook it with herbs and spices and mix with other appropriate ingredients.

- Salmon, like other fish, is of a cooling nature; eat it once or twice a week at most; choose fatty fish, such as halibut, mackerel, tuna or carp and cook them with appropriate spices; never mix them with fruit, fresh salads or fruit juices.

- Do not give up meat completely but modify the way you cook it.

- Cook mostly with lamb, young beef and turkey.

- Drink whole milk as it contains valuable vitamins and mineral salts needed for calcium absorption. Do not drink milk in the morning or on an empty stomach.

- Eat white cheeses together with butter, cream, spices, onion or garlic, but remember that this will not neutralize their cooling nature.

- Low-fat and hard cheeses should be avoided by those who suffer from allergies, asthma, paralysis, diabetes, liver cirrhosis, intestinal problems, colds, flu, tonsillitis, coughs; they should be especially avoided by children and older people. White cheese is good in moderation for those who suffer from liver and heart fire.

- Hard cheese (which is basically a very condensed concentrate of calcium and protein) should be eaten rather rarely.

- Remember that an excess of calcium (Yin) in your diet harms your body; it leads to overcooling and deregulates your cellular metabolism; it can also cause allergies, headaches, joint and muscle pains, kidney and gallstones.

- Remember that within your body, magnesium stands for Yang and calcium stands for Yin. Try to maintain the balance between these two elements.

- It is not true that fresh salads are healthy; they are difficult to digest and have strongly cooling properties.

- By stewing or boiling vegetables you make them easier to digest; therefore, you can eat more vegetables and receive more of the valuable elements: fibre, vitamins and mineral salts.

- The process of cooking does not reduce the quantity of vitamins and mineral salts in your food substantially.

- You only need a small amount of vitamin C; an excess of this vitamin can destroy the liver and kidneys (kidney stones).

- The fashion for eating raw vegetables comes from the 1970s.

- The foundation of all cuisines of the world is cooked or stewed food with a large quantity of spices, garlic and onion.

- Eating large quantities of fresh salads and fruit (even though you are driven by good intentions) will never be of any benefit to your health.

- Frozen food becomes more energetic when cooked or stewed and with the addition of many spices.

- If you really have to use canned food, then at least make sure that you cook it properly (boiling, stewing, etc.) and add a lot of vegetables and spices.

- The chapter on vitamins is meant to make you realize that the most important factor is the interdependence between particular vitamins which affect their absorption; the quantity of vitamins is not as important as their absorption.

- Remember that Chinese, black and green teas are of cooling and drying properties. Chinese people are less susceptible to strokes, diabetes and cancers not because they drink a lot of tea but because they have a well-balanced diet. They drink tea merely to balance out highly warming meals.

- Remember that every single ailment manifests an imbalance within your body.

- Remember that 90% of your aliments are caused by an imbalance within the element of Earth (stomach, spleen and pancreas).

- Remember that the stomach sends out the energy obtained from food to the spleen and that the spleen produces bodily fluids (essence) which nourish the rest of the bodily organs.

- So, do not be surprised that the majority of my recommendations are focused on strengthening the stomach and spleen.

- Remember that the spleen does not tolerate food of cooling properties as well as any sour, raw and cold food (see Tab. 8 and Tab. 9).

- Smoking cigarettes can be beneficial only when suffering from a cold spleen and stomach and during stress. But you must also remember that smoking weakens and destroys the lungs which are responsible for delivering the energy Chi to the heart and the essence to the kidneys. You have to consider then what is most important for you. Perhaps by changing your dietary habits you will be able to strengthen your spleen and quit smoking.

- Alcoholism is typical of people leading a very irregular lifestyle and suffering emotional problems. In many cases they can be helped by eliminating from their diet food products of a cooling nature (e.g. pork, cold drinks) and replacing them with regular meals of a neutral and warming nature.

- If you want to prevent osteoporosis you must remember the importance of vitamins D and A – sunlight, eggs, butter, fatty fish, warming meals, meat and olive oil.

- Every obese person suffers from Yang deficiency. They should eat more neutral and warming food products.

- Remember that cancers usually occur when your body is overcooled and suffering from deregulated cellular metabolism caused mostly by strong emotions, an unwise lifestyle and eating too much food with cooling properties.

- Heart diseases are not directly caused by problems with the teeth; they are caused by a malfunctioning spleen and kidneys, which then leads to dental problems.

- Rotten teeth are a symptom of weakened kidneys, caused by cooling food, stress and low body temperature.

- Any gum problems or problems with the jaw are symptoms of a weak stomach or spleen, as well as intestinal problems and heart fire. You should eliminate all sour, raw and cold food (see Tab. 9) as well as any products of a cooling nature (see Tab. 8).

- Scoliosis is a symptom of a strong weakening within the whole body but most of all a weak spleen (weak muscles), liver (affects the connective tissue), kidneys (deficiency of Yang) and bladder. You should immediately switch to food of neutral and warming properties. You should also start physical exercise.

- If you suffer from asthma then it is most likely that you have a damaged stomach, spleen, kidneys and liver. You should eliminate from your diet all sour, raw and cold food (see Tab. 9) as well as the excess of cooling food (see Tab. 8). You should only eat food of neutral and warming properties.

- If anyone in your family suffers from diabetes then it is most likely that their body is overcooled and they have a damaged stomach, spleen, pancreas, liver and kidneys. They should eliminate from their diet all sour, raw and cold food (see Tab. 9) as well as the excess of cooling food (see Tab. 8); they simply need to restore the Yin of their body.

- If you are breastfeeding then you should remember that your milk will always acquire the nature of the food you are eating. Because of this your baby may suffer pain, vomiting and diarrhoea. Thus be careful and try eating only warm food of neutral or warming properties. Do not avoid garlic or spices. Eliminate, though, all sour, raw and cold food (see Tab. 9).

- Remember that most of your child's health problems are simply side effects of your dietary habits during pregnancy or the breastfeeding period (excess of sour, raw and cold food as well as sweets). But how we feed them while they are growing is also very important. Such food products as milk, cheeses, fruit juices, cold drinks, sweets and all kinds of fast food we should give them in moderation. Instead their diet should contain mild-flavoured and well-balanced meals of a slightly warming nature with no added sugar.

- Remember that soya milk is strongly cooling and should not be given to children susceptible to allergies. Also, replace cow's milk with goat's milk.

- Your children should not be given any sour, raw and cold food (see Tab. 9) until the age of three. This kind of food may prevent the proper development of their bodily organs. You should use sour flavour in minimal quantities only to balance out their meals.

- Older people should mostly eat food of a neutral and warming nature.

- Remember that if you have suffered a stroke or paralysis then you should avoid all sour, raw and cold food (see Tab. 9). I have to repeat here that sour flavour and coldness have a contracting effect on the body. More appropriate in this case would be food of a neutral and warming nature with mild spices.

- If you have suffered a heart attack, or if you think that you are susceptible to one, then you should remember that the quality of your heartbeat depends on the functioning of your spleen and stomach as they pass on the energy to all the other bodily organs. When your body is weakened your spleen starts using up the energy of your heart.

- You should then avoid food that is low in energy. This kind of food will only weaken and overcool your body. Give up sweets and all sour, raw and cold food. Instead I recommend food of a neutral and warming nature as well as physical exercise and avoiding stress.

- If you have problems with your large intestine (haemorrhoids, inflammation, constipation) then you should realize that they are symptoms of a malfunctioning spleen, liver and kidneys. You should eat mostly food of a neutral and warming nature, which will strengthen your stomach and spleen.

- If you suffer from allergies then you should eliminate from your diet all dairy products as well as soya products and soya milk, sweets and any sour, raw and cold food (see Tab. 9). Start eating food of a neutral and warming nature and you will soon forget about allergies.

- Remember that any problems with the hair (dry and splitting hair, hair loss and premature greyness) are symptoms of weakened kidneys (Yang deficiency) as well as a cold liver and spleen. This is mostly caused by stress and inappropriate diet. Start eating warm meals of a neutral and warming nature.

- Any problems with your eyes (short-sightedness, cataracts, glaucoma, wet eyes, sensitivity to light) are symptoms of certain liver conditions (cold liver, stalling of energy, Yin deficiency). You should then give up all sour, raw and cold food (see Tab. 9) as well as food of a cooling nature (see Tab. 8).

- Wrinkly and dry skin signifies weakened kidneys, lungs and liver. You should eliminate all sour, raw and cold food as well as food of a cooling nature. This way you will strengthen the spleen and restore Yin.

- Any skin problems, such as spots and acne, are a result of stress and a hormonal imbalance. But they can also be symptoms of problems with the large intestine, lungs and liver. In this case, you should eliminate from your diet all food with cooling properties and, most of all, sweets, fruit, cold drinks and stop eating too much pork and chicken. You should start eating instead food of a neutral and warming property.

- Your problems with tendons and muscles and susceptibility to contusions are a symptom of a cold spleen and liver. You should give up drinking cold milk and other cold drinks. Also, eliminate from your diet all sour, raw and cold food (see Tab. 9).

- High blood pressure is a symptom of a weakened spleen, liver and kidneys, which is probably caused by stress and/or food of a cooling nature. You should definitely eliminate from your diet all sour, raw and cold food and the excess of food with cooling properties (see Tab. 9 and Tab. 8). Avoid drinking cold water. Very helpful in this case is food of a neutral and warming nature.

- Remember that tonsillitis is a result of stalling of energy in the liver, stomach or large intestine caused by stress, overcooling of your body or an inappropriate diet. To overcome these problems you should eliminate from your diet all sour, raw and cold food (see Tab. 9) and the excess of food of a cooling nature (see Tab. 8). In order to get better you should eat food of a neutral nature.

- Flu can lead to serious side effects (joint inflammation, heart problems) only when you do not warm up your body sufficiently and continue eating sour, raw and cold food.

- Children often suffer from a high body temperature and a sore throat, both of which are caused by indigestion. It is a result of a blocked liver and stomach. You should give them some neutral or slightly warming tea and food of a neutral and warming nature. Any sour, raw and cold food is in this case highly inadvisable (see Tab. 9).

- Coughs are usually a symptom of spleen, lungs and liver problems. If you suffer from dry coughs, drink some Emser salt. Wet coughs are best treated with warming teas or warm milk with honey and garlic.

- If you feel thirsty all the time or have a constantly dry mouth it means that you suffer from a weakened spleen. You should drink only hot teas of neutral and warming properties and eat warming soups. This way you will strengthen your spleen and get rid of the feeling of thirst.

- Remember that AIDS is most likely to develop when your body is weakened (lacking Yin-Yang balance) by an inappropriate diet and lifestyle.

- Viruses and bacteria are active only in certain conditions (as noticed by Pasteur). Thus, once we change those conditions (by strengthening our body) viruses and bacteria will lose their vitality.

- Do not concentrate on getting rid of the viruses and bacteria but on strengthening your own body.

- A very radical war against viruses and bacteria may actually lead to a biological imbalance on Earth.

- If you have some urgent work to do that requires mental stimulation and concentration then do not eat sweets and fat. You should eat food high in protein instead. Sweets relax the body and make you feel sleepy.

- Remember that sweets only increase all kinds of health problems. Sweets acidify the body and damage the spleen.

- Acidification of the body is always caused by eating food that damages the spleen (see Tab. 8 and Tab. 9). If you suffer from hyperacidity or peptic ulcers you should avoid all sour, raw and cold food and an excess of food of a cooling nature.

• If your health is in good condition then you can eat sour, raw and cold food, but always in moderation. Any health problems are an alert to avoid this kind of food.

• The so-called healthy food products such as sprouts, oat bran, nuts, raisins and seeds are of a cooling nature and eaten in excess can damage your spleen.

• Remember that all you put into your mouth is of a specific nature and has an impact on particular bodily organs.

• The so-called dietetic food (with no spices, with no fat and mostly steamed) can only be eaten for a short period of time.

• Do not be afraid of broths. Eat them quite regularly. They are, in fact, very nutritious and strengthening. Remember that a cup of tea has 170 times more purine than a portion of broth.

• You need to use all flavours (sour, bitter, sweet, spicy and salty) in order to balance your daily diet.

• Remember that food of a dominant sour flavour, despite balancing it with other flavours, will always be of a cooling nature (e.g. tomato soup, borscht).

• The sour flavour required to balance your food can be found in lemons, gherkins, tomatoes, greens and basil.

• When preparing a meal or a tea with very strong warming properties, you should avoid adding any sour-flavoured ingredients.

• In everyday cooking you should neutralize an excessive Yang of beef or lamb by adding all Five Flavours (vegetables and spices); you can do the same with buckwheat and neutralize it with, for example, white cheese.

• All food products of the Yin type (vegetables, chicken, fish, pork and cheeses) can be balanced out (made more Yang) by all sorts of cooking processes, such as boiling, roasting, frying, stewing or adding some onion, leeks, garlic and spices, as well as putting them together with other appropriate food products.

- A well-balanced meal is automatically easier to digest. However, you should remember that 'well balanced' does not necessarily mean 'of a warming nature'. Such foods as, for example, tomato soup, will always have cooling properties.

- Strongly warming foods and teas should be used sporadically and for a short period of time and always accompanied by food of a neutral and warming nature.

- Remember to avoid strongly warming food whilst on antibiotics or hormonal medication!

- It is impossible to warm up your body when eating sour, raw and cold food (see Tab. 9) and sweets. This way you can only deregulate the functioning of your bodily organs and the consequences of this can be bad for your health. Compare your body to a car engine. The engine works beautifully when it is warm and has the right fuel. Take time to think whether you are doing the same to yourself; whether you are warm enough and providing your body with the right kind of fuel.

- Remember that the neutral and warming nature of food can only be achieved when the food is balanced with all flavours and cooked with a large quantity of vegetables and other ingredients of a strongly Yang nature, such as beef, onion, garlic and spices.

- Even when you balance your meal with all the flavours and add ingredients of a strongly Yang nature, if the meal has a dominant sour flavour it will always be of a neutral and cooling nature (e.g. tomato soup).

- The last flavour added to your meal will not influence the nature of the meal. It simply directs the energy to a particular bodily organ. For example, if you finish cooking by adding the salty flavour, the energy of your meal will be directed to your kidneys; if it is the sour flavour, to your liver. It is advisable to finish cooking with different flavours, unless you want to strengthen one particular organ. In the latter case, you need to be careful with food of a neutral and cooling nature.

- Do not combine cooling dishes together; for example, sorrel soup with fish and fresh salad.

- You should cook all your food under cover except for during the spring period (from mid February to the end of April) (see Fig. 12). In spring, your food does not need to be overly energizing as the energy of spring and your liver will fulfil all your needs. It does not mean, however, that you should start cooling your body.

- Remember that an overcooled body manifests itself not only through a deficiency of Yang (warmth and energy) but also through malfunctioning of particular bodily organs, deregulated metabolism and Yin deficiency (bodily fluids and essence).

- Remember that an overcooled body has very little room for Yang. This means that an excess of Yang cannot be balanced with an appropriate quality of Yin (fluids and essence).

- Remember that by eliminating from your diet all sour, raw and cold food and introducing well-balanced meals, your menu will not be less exciting than before. In fact, it will become tastier and easier to digest. You can then eat as much as you want and stop being afraid of putting on weight.

- Remember that the most important process in warming up your body is elimination from your diet of all sour, raw and cold food and moderate consumption of sweets.

- Remember that if you have been eating large quantities of fruit, fruit juices and yogurts, you need to start the process of warming up very slowly. You first have to restore the Yin of your body and this process takes a long time.

- Remember that cold water also reduces your Yang.

- Do not snack between meals.

- Try not to drink anything whilst eating a meal.

- Make sure you drink coffee before a meal (e.g. breakfast).

- Boil coffee and add some honey to it, but no milk.

- Instead of sugar, use honey, and in baking, golden sugar.

- Drink tea half an hour before or half an hour after a meal.

- Keep out of sight all fruit, sweets and fruit juices.

- Cook your dinner to last for two days. Make sure that after coming back from work you have at least some soup ready to eat.

- Do not be ashamed to carry your own coffee or tea to work in a thermos flask or to take your own sandwiches.

- Do not be ashamed to refuse to eat something that has been offered to you but which may be harmful to your health (e.g. during a party or a visit).

- Remember that digestion requires fire; that is, warmth and energy.

- Learn to observe the environment and your own body. For this you need a peaceful mind and concentration.

- Organize your day, and make sure you always find some time to relax.

| | Wood - sour | Fire - bitter | Earth – Centre - sweet | Metal - spicy | Water - salty |
|---|---|---|---|---|---|
| Cereals and grains | wheat | buckwheat, rye | millet, corn | rice, oats, barley | beans, soya |
| Vegetables | green parts of vegetables, cereal germ, sprouts, lettuce, pickled gherkins, sauerkraut, tomatoes, sorrel | beet-greens, chicory, artichokes, endive, bitter lettuce, red cabbage | pumpkin, carrots, parsley root, green peas, split peas, potatoes, sweet pepper, beetroot, edible mushrooms, spinach, asparagus, cucumber, pattypan squash, dried vegetables | hot peppers, garlic, leeks, onion, chives, horseradish, white cabbage, Savoy cabbage, Napa cabbage, cauliflower, kohlrabi, broccoli, celeriac, white radish, radish, black turnip | black Chinese mushrooms |
| Fruits | peaches, quince, sour: -grapes, apples, pears, grapefruits, gooseberries, black/white/red currants, strawberries, wild strawberries, lemons, tangerines/clementines, satsumas, oranges, rhubarb | walnuts, dark plums, red grapes, smoked fruits | cherries, black cherries, apricots, raspberries, sweet: -peaches, -grapefruits, -apples, -pears, -raisins, bananas, dates, figs, water melons, pineapples, mango, almonds, pistachios, sunflower seeds, hazelnuts | | peanuts |
| Spices | white wine vinegar, lemon balm, yeast, basil | cocoa, coffee, mugwort, tarragon, wormwood, thyme, sage, marjoram, saffron, turmeric | cinnamon, cumin, linseed, fennel, anise, liquorice, vanilla, cereal milk, sesame, honey, maple syrup, olive oil, mayonnaise | chilli, ginger, allspice, nutmeg, nigella, coriander, black and white pepper, mustard seed, curry, oregano, pepper mint | salt, dried vegetable powder, baking powder |
| Animal products | duck, chicken, sour milk, sour cream, yogurt, kefir, white cheese | lamb, mutton, goat meat, goat milk, goat cheese, sheep's-milk cheese | beef, veal, goose, rabbit, fresh-water fish, cow's milk, butter, sweet cream, eggs | hare, wild boar, deer, pheasant, quail, turkey | pork, pigeon, sea fish, crayfish, frogs, oysters, crabs, blue cheese |
| Herbs and drinks | hibiscus, parsley, birch juice, wheat beer, sour juices, white wine | natural and chicory coffee, cocoa, thyme, red rosemary, ginseng, black and green tea, beer, sage, gentian, dandelion, boiling water | anise, white ginseng, corn silk, linden, camomile, raspberry and blackberry leaves, liquorice | vodka, cognac, whisky, rice wine, ginger tea, cinnamon tea, clove tea | cold water |

Table 7. List of food products according to the Five Elements Theory.

| Dairy products | Cereal products | Cooked food | Fruits and vegetables | Boiled drinks (warm) | Boiled drinks (cold) | Ready-made food products | Sweets | Meat |
|---|---|---|---|---|---|---|---|---|
| hard cheese, processed cheese, white cheese, natural yogurt, fruit yogurts, kefir, sour milk, sour cream, buttermilk, ice cream | wheat flour, semolina, wheat bread, brioche, cakes, biscuits, pasta, white rice | chicken broth, gherkin soup, tomato soup, sorrel soup, young cabbage soup, stewed sauerkraut, tomato sauce, plain boiled bean | all raw fruits, fresh salads, vegetables except for onion, leek and garlic, lettuce, gherkins, sauerkraut | black tea, green tea, camomile tea, peppermint tea, gentian tea | natural coffee, chicory coffee, black tea | beer, fizzy drinks, all kinds of fruit and vegetable juices, mineral water | sugar and all kinds of sweets, chocolate, chocolate bars | chicken, fish, pork, fatback, ham and sausages |

Table 8. Food products of cooling properties.

| Sour | Raw | Cold |
|------|-----|------|
| sauerkraut, gherkins, tomatoes, apples, straw- berries, gooseberries, lemons, oranges, kiwi, grapefruit, white cheese, fruit yogurts, natural yogurt, kefir, buttermilk, fruit juices, fruit milk- shakes, compotes, jams and other products from the element of Wood (see Table 7) | fresh salads, raw vege- tables, all fruits, cereal (eaten raw), all seeds and nuts (eaten raw) | fizzy drinks, soft drinks, water, beer, compotes, fruit and vegetable juices, milk, yogurts, kefir, fruit milkshakes, cold natural coffee, cold chicory coffee, cold tea |

Table 9. Sour, raw and cold food products.